# Hope for Hurting Parents

# Parent Notebook

Tom and Dena Yohe

# DEDICATION

We would like to dedicate this guide to the one who qualified us to write it, without whom it never would have been possible—our daughter, Renee.

It may seem strange that the person who put us in the position of needing this kind of help ourselves, is the one we're dedicating it to, but it's not strange to us at all. That's how God works, turning the wisdom of our culture upside down. He takes the bad and turns it into good. He takes the most embarrassing parts of our lives and creates something we can be proud of out of the ashes.

Renee, having you in our lives gave us the opportunity for greater personal growth than we would have had without you. As your parents, we came face to face with our failures and weaknesses, and today we are not the same. Our experience drove us to search for something we couldn't find and moved us to create something new from the void.

Our mess has become our message.

Our pain has become our passion.

Because of what we went through as your mom and dad, we wrote this Hope for Hurting Parents Parent Notebook. Now, many other hurting parents will come together and find the same comfort we have received from God.

*"Praise be to the God and Father of our Lord Jesus Christ, the Father of compassion and God of all comfort, who comforts us in all our troubles, so that we can comfort those in any trouble, with the same comfort we ourselves have received from God. For just as the sufferings of Christ flow over into our lives, so also through Christ our comfort overflows"* (2 Corinthians 1: 3-5).

# TABLE OF CONTENTS

**GENERAL INFORMATION**

**GROUP SESSIONS**

# THANK YOU

Thank you to the many parents who took the time to tell us how much help they received from our Hope for Hurting Parents support group. We're also grateful to those who wrote to tell us how much they wished they had a group like ours. God used them to prompt us to develop a tool to start more groups

We want to thank those who helped us bring this guide to reality. The following people have given their wisdom, skills, and time to edit our work: Gail Porter, Janet Richards, and Patti Ordower. Pam Findley got behind the vision to publish this Facilitator Guide and the accompanying Parent Notebook. She inspired others whose generously gave to help make it happen. Donni Keene did a wonderful job designing the cover. Thank you to each one of you for your efforts on this project.

Our deepest gratitude is to God who gave us the direction, wisdom, and perseverance needed to work hard until this was finished. He kept our focus on the encouragement, comfort, and hope we wanted these support groups to bring hurting parents.

# MEET TOM AND DENA YOHE

Married thirty-nine years, Tom (M.Div.'79) and Dena have three children and two grandchildren. They served seventeen years in pastoral ministry and fourteen years with CRU (Campus Crusade for Christ), part of that time in Moscow, Russia.

Tom and Dena have a passion to help hurting parents because of their own painful ten year journey with their daughter Renee who has struggled with mental health issues, addiction, and self-injury. They have led support groups for parents like themselves since 2009. In 2011 they co-founded Hope for Hurting Parents, www.HopeforHurtingParents.com. Several years later they wrote this facilitator guide to help others start support groups.

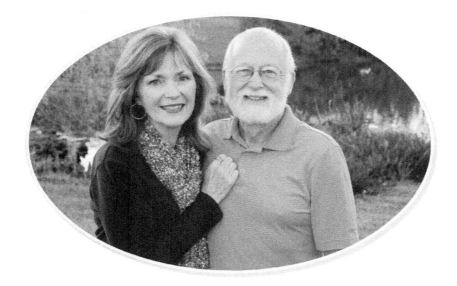

Their mission is to give comfort, encouragement, and hope to hurting parents in their journey from surviving to thriving. This not only takes place in their support groups, but also in a variety of other ways: their website hosts a blog, a sign-up for encouraging emails, recommended books, websites, and resources. Personal meetings, phone calls, Skype appointments, intercessory prayer, social media, speaking and seminars are more ways they offer hope to brokenhearted parents.

In July of 2016, Dena published her book, *You Are Not Alone: Hope for Hurting Parents of Troubled Kids*. Together they have done interviews for TV and radio addressing their ministry and Dena's book. They have been featured on Family Talk with Dr. James Dobson, Family Life with Dennis Rainey and Bob Lepine, and Focus on the Family with Jim Daly and John Fuller.

The story of their daughter Renee's journey and her process of recovery is part of the worldwide movement called To Write Love on Her Arms (twloha.com). A movie was released by Sony in 2015 telling a fictionalized version of that story.

# DENA'S BOOK

*You Are Not Alone*

*Hope For Hurting Parent's
of Troubled Kids*

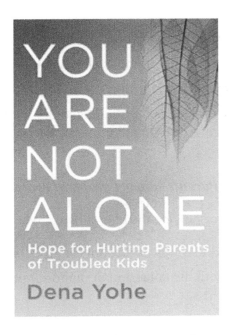

In her book, Dena writes from experience and offers:

*Ideas to keep up your emotional and spiritual well-being when your world
feels as if it's crashing down.

*Suggestions for responding to friends who don't understand.

*Healthy ways to maintain other relationships and more.

*Includes prayers, exercises, websites, and other resources.

"Parents of prodigals often wrestle with feelings of profound loneliness and alienation. In
her moving account, Dena Yohe offers encouraging reminders that countless other
parents have been there too. Her wise and compassionate advice is sure to comfort and
uplift many hurting moms and dads."

Jim Daly, president of Focus on the Family

*Available wherever fine books are sold.*

# MISSION STATEMENT

**Our Mission:** *To give comfort, encouragement, and hope to hurting parents on their journey from surviving to thriving.*

Our Support Groups exist to offer unconditional love and comfort to parents while providing them tools to gain strength and new perspectives.

- Experiencing Love and Comfort – you are not alone; you're safe
- Gaining Strength and Perspective – living each day with the big picture in view
- Building Courage and Hope – if things don't resolve, God is still there
- We do this because: parents often feel discouraged, hopeless, and isolated when dealing with a child/children who have gone "prodigal" from the family.

**Our Passion:** *A Hope for Hurting Parents support group in every community.*

We want to reach any parent inside or outside the church walls who is dealing with a child*:

- Who is abusing or addicted to drugs or alcohol (or any other addiction).
- Who has repeat offenses with the court and/or authority problems with the school system or is incarcerated.
- Who brings physical harm to themselves such as self-injury (cutting), suicide attempts or an eating disorder.
- Who defies parental boundaries by running away.
- Who engages in sexual behaviors, pornography, or has gender identity issues.
- Who has a mental illness and isn't coping well, making destructive decisions.

*This child can be any age, teen or adult.

# WHAT OTHERS ARE SAYING

**Parents**

> "I really needed this tonight. Being with others who understand and don't judge me is so freeing. My heart feels so much lighter. I really needed the topic of detachment, too. I have a lot to work on, but now I feel like I can do it!"

> "About 4 years ago, I felt very alone with my situation experiencing much chaos in my life with my son living in the house addicted to drugs and alcohol. I felt like I was beginning to slip into a pattern of internalizing everything that was happening feeling very angry, sad, depressed and hopeless that things would never change. I decided I would try a group and keep an open mind. If it didn't work or it was too awkward, I wouldn't go again.
>
> It was so helpful I decided I would keep going as much as I could and looked forward to the next meeting. The topics were relevant and interactive. It was very healing to discuss my situation and feelings. I liked hearing from other moms who were experiencing pain with their teens or adult children."

> "I really appreciated the topic in print. I had something tangible I could hang on to and look at again and again during times of crisis, offering scripture and hope. Most of all, the group supported me with their prayers, which helped me to regain my focus on God's strength instead of my own. I now realize that my son's situation is not hopeless."

> "We cannot thank you enough for your ministry. Over the past year, as we worked through the various stages of facing our son's choices, you have been there alongside us. Your ministry and group have been a real safe haven for us to catch our breaths."

> "Opening your home and offering warm hospitality, non-judgmental input, real-life empathy and shoulders to cry on, has been a real blessing for us (and I do not throw that word around lightly). And we know this is true for the many others who have stepped across your threshold. Your transparency with your own personal story has been courageous and humbling. You have encouraged us in numerous ways and we feel a strong bond of suffering with you both that we don't (can't) share with anyone else in our lives."

> "It was such a pleasure to be in the group. It is very comforting to know you're not alone. I was encouraged and found the handout helpful. I am thankful to be in a group where people share openly, and don't feel judged. It's been a long road, and I'm so encouraged after the meeting yesterday. I am truly glad and feel so much more at peace knowing that I have a safe place with others who share the same types of struggles."

**Group Facilitators**

> "Thank you for your ministry. Our group is going well. The guide is a God send. Please continue this work."

> "The content is very rich and filled with wisdom. We have all felt that the material is very insightful and useful for us in our journey. There are many times we have shared how 'right on' the material is in helping us navigate this uncharted territory."

> The topics are so relevant in your guide. I think every parent experiencing these types of situations can relate to them at some point in their journey with an adult child.
> Leading a Hope for Hurting Parents group is very meaningful to me. God keeps leading me to others who are hurting. God used my situation to give me more compassion and encourage others in similar situations.
>
> One woman in my group commented, 'Everyone needs a group like Hope for Hurting Parents.' She is right. I have talked to women in other states who have never heard it and are interested in having one. There is a need for groups like these to love, support, pray for, and encourage one another through our struggles."

## Church and Ministry Leaders

> "A Hope for Hurting Parents group provides immeasurable support, guidance, hope, and care to those who attend. I have watched and witnessed the profound affect this group provides to the hurting parents of our church community."
> *Berry Johnston - Pastor of C.A.R.E. Ministries, Discovery Church, Orlando, FL*

> "I have had the privilege of getting to know Tom and Dena Yohe and their ministry, Hope for Hurting Parents. The Yohes have a tremendous testimony and are faithful witnesses to the healing power of Christ. We at New Covenant United Methodist Church have two Hope for Hurting Parents groups now. We seek their wise counsel and advice as we move through this process. I cannot think of better representatives for the Kingdom than the Yohes who we can journey alongside."
> *Ellen Pollock – Director of Congregational Care Ministry, New Covenant United Methodist Church, The Villages, FL*

> "The beauty of what happens in a Hope for Hurting Parents support group has been so inspiring to us at Village View Church. The group is a safe place for participants to take their hurt, let it out, then leave with the hope they need to make it through another day with the strength of Jesus Christ guiding every step."
> *Deb Williams – former Recovery and Support Ministries Pastor, Village View Community Church, Summerfield, FL*

> "Tom and Dena Yohe have lived through the ups and downs, and hurts and joys of life with a prodigal. All they have learned is now helping so many others through their wonderful ministry, Hope for Hurting Parents. They not only have wise encouragement, but also powerful prayers."
> *Judy Douglass - Writer, Speaker, Encourager, Founder Prayer for Prodigals Campus Crusade for Christ, International (Cru)*

> "I would like to recommend Tom and Dena Yohe's ministry, Hope for Hurting Parents. In the words of one of the parents attending their small group, 'I just love these two people. They have helped me so much to understand my role as a parent. I felt like I was really helped. It really is important that I attend these sessions.' "
> *Pastor Marty Shea - Senior Pastor, Village View Community Church, Summerfield, FL*

## Mental Health Professionals

> "Tom and Dena are passionate and devoted to their cause. They can personally identify with parents who are struggling to raise and deal with difficult children. They also help families with adult children who are still problematic. I love what they are doing and want to continue to see their ministry grow so they can help as many hurting families as possible."
> *Debbie Haughton - Licensed Mental Health Counselor, Orlando Counseling Services, Orlando, FL*

> "These support groups provide a safe place to feel, share, and encourage one another as hurting parents who are on a journey through parenting challenges with adolescent or adult children. The groups are warm, intimate and confidential. The facilitators guide parents with hope through their many resources. I often refer hurting parents to Hope for Hurting Parents as it is a crucial piece of the healing process. I'm excited to see this group multiply and bless others!"
> *Tanya Alvarado, MA, LMHC, New Path Counseling, Orlando, FL*

> "No one should suffer alone. This support group was designed to come alongside of hurting parents. It is safe and parents can come with their authentic selves to receive love and support without judgement. I know of no other group like it. I personally have felt buoyed up and prayed for during some of my most difficult parenting days and continue to find those who supported me a continued support today. It is a gift to carry one another's burdens and share in their pain side by side. It is an experience of Jesus being present to heal the brokenhearted."
> *Nancy A. Johnson, EdD, LMHC*

> "As a parent of two sons who struggle with mental health concerns, I personally know the value of a caring, knowledgeable support network. This group provides that and more. The discussions are open and honest; the information shared is practical and understandable; the relationships formed are invaluable. I highly recommend this group to my clients who are parents seeking to love their child well in the difficult times."
> *Mike Wilcox, M.A., M.A., LMHC, Pinnacle Counseling Institute, Orlando, FL*

# WELCOME TO HOPE FOR HURTING PARENTS: WHAT TO EXPECT

We applaud you for admitting your need for help and taking the step to come to one of our support groups. From personal experience as hurting parents ourselves, we believe this is the best thing you could do for yourself. We hope you'll soon realize how helpful it is to be with other parents who *get it*, who understand what you are going through. Unlike most of your friends and family, they know how you feel. This group can be a wonderful source of encouragement and support.

We've traveled this dark, troubling road. We know how isolating it can be. That's why, in 2009, we started our first support group. We wanted to offer a safe, confidential, accepting, and nurturing environment for parents whose children were causing them pain and heartache.

**What is the focus For the group?**

The focus is you, the parent. It's to help you process your feelings about the situation with your child so you can be emotionally and spiritually healthy. This may disappoint you, but this group is not a place to learn how to fix or change your son or daughter. We wish we could do that, but we can't. This is a place you can be authentic and real, accepted as you are, and no one will think less of you.

**Who is this for?**

This group is for parents whose children (adolescents or adults of any age) are making dysfunctional and deeply troubling decisions. As their parents, we're often too close to the situation to make the best decisions. Sometimes the issues are far beyond our ability to understand or cope. We feel clueless how to help them, much less ourselves.

This group is not for parents whose children are simply misbehaving: not doing their school work, completing chores, or being argumentative. It's for parents whose children are engaging in addictive and destructive behaviors: substance abuse (drugs or alcohol), an eating disorder, same-sex identity issues, self-harm, mental health issues, trouble with the law, etc.

**WHy A Notebook?**

This notebook provides the content that will be used in the activities and discussions during your meetings. Each session also includes a page for note-taking or journaling your personal thoughts. These notes can be a valuable part of your journey.

It is our prayer that in this group you will find the encouragement, comfort, and hope you've been looking for.

*Tom and Dena Yohe, co-founders of Hope for Hurting Parents*

# GROUP GUIDELINES

1. This group is not a Bible Study but we refer to scripture; it's not a prayer meeting but we will pray for you and your children. It's not a place to find out how to fix your child, but what you learn may aid their growth.

2. This group is for you, the parent. You are the focus. It's a place for you to process feelings, talk about the struggles you're having with your child, grow personally and be encouraged by others who share similar pain.

3. This group is a confidential and safe place. What's said here stays here and who you meet here stays here. However, you are welcome to share the content and principles you learn here. If you see someone from the group in a public setting, be careful to not make comments about their child's situation that could embarrass them or compromise their privacy.

4. This group is a judgment free zone. We offer unconditional acceptance to one another. We are not here to compare each other's situations or invalidate each other's pain by minimizing what they may be going through.

5. Our goal is to be the best listeners we can be. Please don't interrupt each other or offer *unsolicited* advice. If asked, you are welcome to offer your ideas or insights, otherwise talk with the person after the group.

6. You never need to share or talk in this group. Participate only as you desire. But please be time conscious when sharing, so everyone will have the opportunity to talk.

7. All the content you hear may not always apply to you. We encourage you to take what you like and leave the rest.

8. Contact List: Each time we meet we'll pass around a sheet of paper for you to write down your name, phone number and/or email, so you can develop connections with each other and support one another outside the group time. Be sure to take some names and numbers with you, or simply take a picture of the list with your phone!

# Session 1

# GRIEF AND LOSS

# GRIEF AND LOSS

## Definition

Dictionary.com definition: "keen mental suffering or distress over affliction or loss; sharp sorrow; painful regret." It is a normal emotional response to significant loss, not only from death; the loss of health (diabetes, cancer, etc.), a job, miscarriage, or divorce. The process of adjustment to a major loss; processed differently for each person (personality, past experiences, etc.). Hurting parents experience grief and loss too; not necessarily from death, but from the loss of relationship, the loss of dreams and hopes they had for their son or daughter. People experience a wide range of feelings and symptoms.

## Five Stages of Grief  (by Elisabeth Kubler-Ross)

1.  Shock (I can't believe this is happening.)
2.  Denial (My child wouldn't do that.); Bargaining (God, I'll do _____ if you'll do _____.)
3.  Anger (Why is this happening to me? What did we do wrong?)
4.  Depression (I'm too sad to go to work. Will I ever laugh again?)
5.  Acceptance (I'm at peace with what has happened or whatever is going to happen.)

Grief is a process that takes time.

It's possible to skip around and revisit these stages. At times you may feel: numb, guilty, anxious, fearful, unable to focus or concentrate, a desire to withdraw, irritable, more forgetful, extreme fatigue, restless, health problems worsen or develop new ones.

Possible physical symptoms: dizziness, rapid heartbeat, a lump or tightness in your throat, pressure on your chest, headaches, sleeplessness, loss of appetite, or increased appetite.

Which of these have you felt?  They are signals you are grieving.

## Three Questions to Help Process Grief

1.  What have you lost?

Possible answers: hopes and dreams we had for your child; what might have been and what their lives would have been like; graduation from high school or college; to have a good job; get married; grandchildren; a loving, close relationship; financial resources (counseling, rehab, doctors, lawyers, legal fees, etc.); possessions (things get borrowed, disappear or end up in a pawn shop); time from work; sleep; your health; some friendships; peace of mind; your marriage; relationships with other children; your reputation; if we aren't careful you can even lose your faith.

2. What do you have left?

Possible answers: your other relationships; spouse, other children, friends, God, your work and hobbies, your life—you do still have one. You have a purpose. How can you use this for good?

Don't let your child become the sole focus of your world. You have to get on with living your life with joy and peace again.

3. How can you cope? Here are three steps to help you grieve in a healthy way.

- Learn to accept that your loss is real and you are grieving.
  - You have lost something significant and important.
  - You can't get it back; your life has changed forever; you will never be the same.
  - Take time to remember good memories from the past; it wasn't all bad.
- Give yourself permission to feel the pain.
  - It's emotional and physical; you can't avoid it; don't stuff it or deny it. Let yourself feel the pain, and get it out. Denying can make you sick or prolong the grieving process.
  - It's okay to distract yourself, but not for too long—working longer hours, staying busy, eating more.
  - Don't minimize it or seek to escape it—sleeping more or self-medicating.
  - Talk to a trusted friend, keep a journal if you like to write, express yourself in creative ways if you have this talent.
- Adjust to your new normal.
  - Shift your focus to other people and healthy activities.
  - Try to keep doing your normal, daily tasks as much as you can.
  - Give yourself permission to cry or be angry; feel whatever you're feeling. It's okay.
  - Talk about how you feel; don't let others tell you how you should feel.

- Take care of yourself—exercise, take naps if needed, eat healthy, and get adequate rest.
- Ask for help if you need it—see a counselor or your pastor; go to your doctor for a checkup; you may need medication temporarily.

George Bananno states in his book *The Other Side of Sadness*, "Grieving is not static but involves a regular oscillation." These are periods or cycles when you fluctuate in and out of laughter even joy in the midst of the waves of sadness. Positive emotions and smiling bring some relief. While it sounds contradictory, his research found that those who have this capacity will grieve in the healthier way and be more resilient.

It's important to learn to grieve well because it's critical to survival and finding joy in hard times. Otherwise you will live in defeat and lose your joy.

## Scripture

Psalm 34:18
"The LORD is close to the brokenhearted and saves those who are crushed in spirit."

2 Corinthians 1:3–4
"Praise be the God and Father of our Lord Jesus Christ, the Father of compassion and the God of all comfort, who comforts us in all our troubles, so that we can comfort those in any trouble with the comfort we ourselves receive from God."

Proverbs 17:22
"A cheerful heart is good medicine, but a crushed spirit dries up the bones."

Revelation 21:4
"He will wipe every tear from their eyes. There will be no more death or mourning or crying or pain, for the old order of things has passed away."

# NOTES

# Session 2

# ENABLING

# ENABLING

## Definition

Enabling is reacting to a person in such a way to shield them from experiencing the full impact of the harmful consequences of their behavior. It differs from helping in that it permits or allows the person to be irresponsible (Celebrate Recovery).

Enabling is doing for someone what they could and should be doing for themselves. Helping is doing something for someone that they can't do for themselves.

## Enabling Behaviors

Change isn't easy. Our enabling behaviors may be a pattern we've had for a long time. We must decide what we're going to do. Remember, enabling may help our children deny their deep problems. If we've played a part, it must stop.

Hebrews 12:11  ESV
"For the moment all discipline seems painful rather than pleasant, but later it yields the peaceful fruit of righteousness to those who have been trained by it."

## Why We Enable

As parents, we enable because:
- We have confused helping with enabling.
- We love too much, too little, and too conditionally.
- We fear for our child's safety, consequences, and the what-ifs.
- We feel guilty about what we did or didn't do.
- We never dealt with our own painful past, including abandonment, abuse, addictions, and other painful circumstances that made us who we are today.
- Our personality traits make us tend to do this.
- It's what we've been doing (habit).
- It's easier than changing.

- It feels like the right thing to do.
- We think our child is disabled or handicapped due to their addiction.
- We're short-sighted and don't know any better.

(Concepts from *Setting Boundaries with Your Adult Children* by Allison Bottke )

## Identifying our Own Issues

We must ask ourselves these hard questions to understand why we enable. It will take courage to identify our own issues.

1. What reward are you getting from enabling?
2. What need is this filling in your life?
   - I feel like I've been helpful.
   - It makes me feel better.
   - I need to be in control.
   - It feels good. I like to help.
   - I'm a fixer. It feels like loving—if I do this, maybe they'll respond back to me in a loving way.
   - I think it will guarantee their acceptance. I feel more secure in our relationship.
   - I'm protecting my pride and good reputation (and theirs) – if they fall, I'll look like a bad parent. What will others think of me – of them?

We need to work on being healthy ourselves. When we don't need to enable or feel rewarded for doing so, we'll find the strength to say, "No, I'm sorry_____, but I decided I can't or won't be helping you with that anymore. But I'm confident you will solve this problem on your own. You can do it!"

Remember, when we stop enabling, those around us may change too, but there's no guarantee we'll like those changes. We need to stop enabling because it's the right thing for us to do, because it's best for us, not just because of how we hope it will affect our child.

## Four Reminders

- Change is not easy. We can pray for the power to change ourselves.
- By not enabling we can help our children of any age develop wings to fly on their own.
- We can find comfort in knowing we are not alone on this journey.

- We can take back our lives.

## Scripture

Joshua 1:9 ESV

"Have I not commanded you? Be strong and courageous. Do not be frightened, and do not be dismayed, for the LORD your God is with you wherever you go."

Philippians 4:13 NKJV

"I can do all things through Christ who strengthens me."

2 Timothy 1:7 CEV

"God's Spirit doesn't make cowards out of us. The Spirit gives us power, love, and self-control."

# ENABLING SURVEY

1. Have personal belongings mysteriously disappeared from your home?

2. Have you finished a project your child left undone because it was easier than asking them to do it?

3. Did you pay for education or job training more than once?

4. Does your child use profanity, violence, or other unacceptable behavior toward you without consequences?

5. Do you repeatedly give second chances?

6. Do you continuously loan them money and rarely get paid back?

7. Do you have concerns about your finances because of helping them?

8. Have you avoided talking about hard things because you're afraid of their reaction?

9. Are you worried about the damage to your marriage due to the strain from your child?

10. Has there been increased resentment from their siblings or other relatives?

11. Do you now, or have you paid your adult child's bills?

12. Do you pay their cell phone bill so you can contact them?

13. Have you bailed them out of jail or paid for a lawyer more than once?

14. Do they have money for nonessentials (cigarettes, tattoos, movies, etc.) yet need to borrow money from you?

15. Have you asked your adult child (who lives with you) to pay rent but they refuse?

16. Have you given ultimatums but didn't follow through?

17. Have you ever called in sick or made excuses for them?

18. Do you wonder why they can't get or keep a job?

19. Do you feel like there's nothing else you can do for them?

20. Are you mad at yourself for what you've been doing?

*These are adapted from Allison Bottke's Enabling Survey in her book *Setting Boundaries with Your Adult Children.*

# NOTES

# Session 3

# GUILT

# GUILT

We've all felt guilty at times over the situation with our child. It seems to be part of the "why" question. There must be some reason. Maybe it's my fault? We ask ourselves painful questions: "What did I do wrong?" "How could my child be this way?" "How could I have prevented this?"

## Definition

A feeling of responsibility or remorse for some offense, crime, or wrong, etc., whether real or imagined. Self-reproach; self-blame; feeling at fault for something.

Rate yourself on a scale of 1 to 10 (10 being high): How guilty do you feel today? Why did you choose that number?

## The Perfect Parent

Even the best parents look for an explanation for their own failures. They say, "If I'd only . . ." and "If I just hadn't . . ." On and on they examine their parenting record, looking for that moment, that mistake that flipped the switch in their relationship.

Let's look at a parent who did it all perfectly and had no guilt.
Read Scripture: Genesis 1:31 and 3:6; Isaiah 1:2 and 5:1–4.

Genesis 1:31 and 3:6

"And God saw everything that he had made, and behold, it was very good. And there was evening and there was morning, the sixth day."
"So when the woman saw that the tree was good for food, and that it was a delight to the eyes, and that the tree was to be desired to make one wise, she took of its fruit and ate, and she also gave some to her husband who was with her, and he ate."

Isaiah 1:2

"Hear, O heavens, and give ear, O earth; for the LORD has spoken: "Children have I reared and brought up, but they have rebelled against me.""

Isaiah 5:1–4

"Let me sing for my beloved my love song concerning his vineyard: My beloved had a vineyard on a very fertile hill. He dug it and cleared it of stones, and planted it with choice vines; he built a watchtower in the midst of it, and hewed out a wine vat in it; and he looked for it to yield grapes, but it yielded wild grapes. And now, O inhabitants of Jerusalem and men of Judah, judge between me and my vineyard. What more was there to do for my vineyard that I have not done in it? When I looked for it to yield grapes, why did it yield wild grapes?"

What truths about parenting do you see in these passages?

Perfect parenting does not guarantee results. We may even get an unexpected outcome. Parents with rebellious children are in good company. Even God's children rebelled.
How does this truth affect your level of guilt?

## What Can We Do About Our Guilt?

1. Ask God to bring to mind any sin and confess it. Be honest without morbid introspection. He will forgive and remove your guilt. God may reveal that you need to ask your child for forgiveness; doing this can have a huge impact on them.

2. Find a safe person and honestly share your struggle with guilt.

3. Don't own your child's problems. Remember, they're making a choice. They are accountable to God for the things they do.

4. False guilt—there's no reason for it; own what you need to own and refuse the rest; learn to recognize Satan's lies; ask God to show you what they are and then to remove them.

5. Let go of the past and move forward; you can't change what has been done. Give yourself *a lot* of grace; you've never done this before; with God's help you're doing the best you can.

## Scripture

Psalm 25:11 ESV
"For your name's sake, O LORD, pardon my guilt, for it is great."

Isaiah 6:7
"See, this has touched your lips; your guilt is taken away and your sin atoned for."

1 John 1: 9 ESV

"If we confess our sins, he is faithful and just to forgive us our sins and to cleanse us from all unrighteousness."

Romans 8:1 ESV

"There is therefore now no condemnation for those who are in Christ Jesus."

Ephesians 6:11

"Put on the full armor of God so that you can take your stand against the devil's schemes."

# NOTES

# Session 4

# COPING WITH FEAR

# COPING WITH FEAR

Fear is Satan's best weapon against us. It is our number one enemy. It ties us up in knots, paralyzes us, weakens our faith, robs us of peace and joy, and causes us to enable our children. It causes us to believe Satan's lies and forget what is true. It's one of our biggest problems as hurting parents.

## Definition

A distressing emotion aroused by impending danger, evil, pain, etc., whether the threat is real or imagined; the feeling or condition of being afraid. Synonyms: foreboding, apprehension, consternation, dismay, dread, terror, fright, panic, horror, trepidation, qualm. (dictionary.com) It causes us to be nervous, worried, and anxious. It's one of the four major emotions—mad, sad, glad, and scared.

**An acrostic for fear: <u>F</u>alse <u>E</u>vidence <u>A</u>ppearing <u>R</u>eal**

**Identifying Our Fears**

**1. What are some things you fear for your child?**

**2. How does fear affect you?**

Possible answers: inability to sleep; loss of appetite or overeating; feeling anxious, nervous, and stressed; physical illness—ulcers, headaches, intestinal problems, chest pain; more emotional than usual; less patient, more irritable, shorter fuse; become more controlling with your child; begin enabling to protect; can be consumed by fear; can't stop thinking about it or talking about it; absorbs all of your thoughts; it takes over; may feel a need to self-medicate for relief (alcohol, nicotine, coffee, sugar); turn to forms of escape—TV, reading, internet, work, hobbies (not necessarily harmful things).

**How We Cope**

- Think positively: "I'm going to be okay." "It could be worse." "I'm not alone."

- Focus on what you can be thankful for instead of the negative.
- Read Psalm 23 before bed, especially verse 2, "He makes me lie down in green pastures."
- Prayer: keep a prayer journal and record answers; this increases your faith.
- Remind yourself God loves your child more than you do. He's not finished.
- Be honest about your fearful feelings. Verbalize your fears to yourself or someone else.

## Coping Suggestions

1. Feed your faith

   Faith thrives on truth and makes it grow stronger. Read scripture, memorize verses, listen to uplifting music, read helpful books, attend worship services, etc.

2. Focus on truth

   God is with us; we are not alone; He will help us; He wants to help our child; He's able to do the impossible; He will never stop trying to reach them; He will use everything for good in their lives and in ours. Search the scriptures for verses that address fear and fill your mind with them. Here's a great one:

   > "But now, this is what the LORD says—
   > 'Do not fear, for I have redeemed you;
   > I have summoned you by name, you are mine;
   > When you pass through the waters, I will be with you;
   > and when you pass through the rivers (at flood stage), they will not sweep over you.
   > When you walk through the fire (of affliction and suffering), you will not be burned;
   > the flames will not set you ablaze.
   > For I am the Lord your God, the Holy One of Israel, your Savior . . .
   > Since you are precious and honored in my sight, and because I love you . . .
   > Do not be afraid, for I am with you.' (Isaiah 43: 1–5)."

3. Avoid fantasy faith

   Convincing ourselves everything will be fine; it's going to be okay; nothing bad is going to happen. She won't get pregnant, he won't end up in jail, they won't become an alcoholic, etc. Something bad could happen.

   We don't know what the outcome will be. We have no guarantees our child will survive or return home safely.

4. Let fear draw you closer to God

   We learn to rely more, trust more, pray more, read the Bible more, and attend worship services. Do everything we can to spiritually strengthen ourselves.

5. Face your fears

   - Facing our fears disarms them. They no longer have as much power over us.
   - Remember God is with us. Take Him into this part of our journey.
   - Here's a good slogan: "Fear knocked on the door. Faith answered and no one was there!"
   - Ask yourself, "What does God have for me in this fearful time?"
   - Accept the what-ifs and make peace with them.
   - We may need the help of a professional counselor or minister.

**Suggestions To Try at Home:**

- Pray for God to help you trust Him with your fears instead of dwelling on them.
- Pray for reassurance of His presence.
- Pray for increased faith and how you can feed yours.
- Spend more time praying than being fearful. Use scripture for your prayers.
- Find a prayer partner who has experienced being fearful over a wayward child.
- Read John 14:27; Jesus gives you His peace and tells you not to be afraid.

# NOTES

# Session 5

# DETACHMENT

# DETACHMENT

**Definition**

Indifferent, aloof, and withdrawn from; to be disconnected, disinterested, isolated, and unconcerned; avoiding emotional involvement. To unfasten and separate; disengage, disunite (dictionary.com).

Perhaps this is why detachment feels so confusing or even wrong for many parents. This is not what is meant when you hear, "We need to detach."

Detachment is neither kind nor unkind. It does not imply judgment or condemnation of the person from whom we are detaching. Separating ourselves from the adverse effects of another person's destructive behaviors is detaching.

This doesn't always require physical separation. Detachment is not separating from the person we care about, but from the agony of our involvement with them. Detachment can help us be more objective about the situation.

Recovery proponents teach there is nothing we can say or do to cause or stop a person's destructive behavior. We're not responsible for our child's problems or their recovery from them. Detachment allows us to let go of our obsession with our child so we can have healthier lives—lives with dignity, guided by God. We can still love them without liking their behavior.

## Through Detachment We Can Learn

- Not to suffer because of the actions or reactions of other people.
- Not to allow ourselves to be used or abused by others in the interest of their recovery.
- Not to do for others what they can do for themselves.
- Not to manipulate situations so others will eat, go to bed, get up, pay bills, not drink or use drugs, or behave the way we want them to.
- Not to cover up for someone else's mistakes or failures.
- Not to prevent a crisis if one happens as life unfolds.

## Things to Remember

The process of detaching is stressful for everyone in the family because human nature usually sees significant change as stressful. It can be just as difficult for us to change our own patterns of behavior as it is for our child. Old habits die hard.

Learning to detach brings another new reality: a letting go of our attempts to control, of denying our own feelings and needs, and of the false belief that our child has to be okay before we can be okay. These changes cause an upheaval in the family system. Everyone must readjust.

Living with the effects of someone else's destructive behavior is too much for most people to bear alone. The feeling of powerlessness over our child can cause us to feel overwhelmed by fear, helplessness, grief, confusion, and a lack of understanding. We don't know what to do next.

Reading helpful materials, attending support groups, meeting with a counselor, and practicing other self-care actions can lessen this stress.

By learning to focus on ourselves, allowing our loved one to experience the consequences of their own actions, our well-being will improve. This can be hard. We'll need a lot of courage.

## Scripture

Joshua 1:9

"Have I not commanded you? Be strong and courageous. Do not be afraid; do not be discouraged, for the LORD your God will be with you wherever you go."

Ephesians 6:10

"Finally, be strong in the LORD and in His mighty power."

# NOTES

# Session 6

# WORRY AND ANXIETY

# WORRY AND ANXIETY

It doesn't make sense to worry yourself sick about things that are not in your control. Worry gives a false sense of control over something we can't do anything about. Not all of life's troubles have a happy ending. Sometimes there's good reason to be anxious. Worry is a common response. Sometimes we can't stop; it becomes chronic, even obsessive and irrational. It can get out of control. Then our ability to think clearly and make good decisions is compromised.

**Four Steps to Help Regain Peace of Mind**

1. Make a physical change

   • The next time you feel yourself worrying uncontrollably, stop and look in a mirror. Notice the tension in your forehead and eyes, your clenched jaw, frown, and stooped posture. Worry takes a toll on our bodies.

   • Breathe deeply. Take a deep breath and another one. Deep and slow. In through your nose, out through your mouth. It will slow your pulse, clear your mind, and relax your muscles. When we worry we tend to hold our breath. We take shallow, short breaths, which heightens anxiety. Give yourself more oxygen—it can do wonderful things for your well-being and it's free.

   • Take a long walk, then a warm bath or shower. Connecting with the beauty of nature is relaxing. Direct your gaze upward and really look at the sky. Let it remind you how great God is. Aerobic exercise and getting a massage are other ways to release worry. Discover what you like and make yourself do it.

2. Change things or change your attitude

   • Realize that being anxious about someone you have no control over won't make them change. It's wasted energy. It can't add even a day to our lives (Matthew 6:27).

   • Try to change something you can—your attitude. Change negative self-talk—"Not this again." "Why does it always have to happen?" "Just what I was afraid of." "They'll never change."—into positive self-talk. Otherwise you'll remain trapped in the problem.

- Supportive self-talk is a healthier remedy. Replace anxious thoughts with truth and positive thoughts: "I know God will help me." "This too shall pass." "With God's help I can handle whatever comes." "Somehow, it will all work out." "Let go and let God."

- Use laughter and humor as a distraction. Watch a funny movie or call someone who uplifts you.

- If you're in a "worrywart rut," listen to soothing music or listen to something encouraging.

3. Turn it over

- Prayer and meditation on God and His Word can soothe your mind and soul. Instead of worrying, pray. Let your worry be your prayer. We know we need to give it to God, but how slow we are to do it.

- Let go of your worries by handing them over to God. There's nothing we can do about them, but we can give them to the One who can do something.

- Philippians 4:6–7 says, "Do not be anxious about anything, but in everything, by prayer and petition, with thanksgiving, present your requests to God. And the peace of God, which transcends all understanding, will guard your hearts and your minds in Christ Jesus."

- Make an exchange—your worry for God's peace.

4. Move outside yourself in gratitude and trust

- Look for someone you can help. A small act of kindness can boost your spirit and distract you from your own troubles. It also has a way of reminding you of your blessings.

- Gratitude is another good antidote for worry. It's rather difficult to worry and be grateful at the same time! Making a list of what we can be thankful for helps keep our worries in their proper perspective.

- Trust is another key to overcoming worry. Ask God to help you trust Him more, as well as yourself and the supportive people around you. Bad things do happen, but we can trust and be confident that whatever happens, we will have or be given by God what we need to handle the situation.

**Scripture**

Matthew 6:25, 27, 33–34 NASB

"Do not be worried about your life. . . . Who of you by being worried can add a single hour to his life? . . . But seek first His kingdom and His righteousness, and all these things will be added to you. So do not worry about tomorrow; for tomorrow will care for itself. Each day has enough trouble of its own."

Philippians 4:6–7

"Do not be anxious about anything, but in every situation, by prayer and petition, with thanksgiving, present your requests to God. And the peace of God, which transcends all understanding, will guard your hearts and your minds in Christ Jesus."

1 Peter 5:7

"Cast all your anxiety on him because he cares for you."

Psalm 94:19

"When anxiety was great within me, your consolation brought me joy."

# NOTES

# Session 7

# ANGER

# ANGER

Many of us react without thinking when confronted with the unacceptable choices of our rebellious child. Sadly, our emotional responses do very little to help the situation. Let's define anger and some of its consequences.

## Definition

A strong feeling of displeasure and belligerence aroused by a wrong; irritation or aggravation (dictionary.com).

Some of us tend to tone it down and say we're frustrated when we are really mad. It's okay to be angry. Psychologists say it is one of the four main emotions—mad, sad, glad, and scared. It's what we do with our feelings of anger that's important. This also applies to anger we may feel toward God. He already knows if we are and He's big enough to take it.

James 1:19–20: "Know this, my beloved brothers: let every person be quick to hear, slow to speak, slow to anger; for the anger of man does not produce the righteousness of God.

## Finding the Source of Our Anger

Our anger can be the result of our inability to be in control of other people's choices and actions. How often have you had this attitude: if only they would listen to my advice and do what I say, these things would not be happening. The scriptures warn us, "In your anger do not sin; do not let the sun go down while you are still angry" (Ephesians 4:26). God wants us to sort through our anger, find its source, and learn how to handle it.

## Questions to Ask Yourself

1. In what ways does your child make you mad?
2. What do you think is the underlying issue?
3. What do you have control over?
4. What changes would you like to make?

**Five Steps to Handling Anger**

"A soft answer turns away wrath, but a harsh word stirs up anger" (Proverbs 15:1).

1. Acknowledge that you're angry.
2. When you feel angry, don't resort to your typical negative response.
3. Find the focus of your anger. Ask yourself, "Why am I angry?"
4. Think about your options. How can you respond in a constructive way?
5. Take constructive action to resolve your anger.

# ANGER WORKSHEET

How would you describe yourself when you're angry?

In what ways does your child make you mad?

What can happen when our anger is out of control?

# PEACEFUL DISCUSSION GUIDE

1. Whenever possible, plan when and where you will talk.

2. Write down what the issues are.

3. Agree ahead of time to not attack each other personally. If one of you begins to attack, stop the discussion.

4. Agree that either person can call a time-out to regain control of their emotions. Choose a specific amount of time. This gives a chance to cool down and refocus.

5. If tempers begin to flare, a good phrase to memorize is, "Honey, I'm not the enemy."

6. Don't be caught by surprise. When you're approached unexpectedly, simply tell the other person you're not prepared to talk. Agree on a time and place for a discussion.

7. Be honest and show respect. The goal is to have peaceful discussions, not to win an argument.

8. Think about how you can end the discussion. For example: "I hear what you're saying and I'll think about it."

9. Before your discussion, try to call a trusted friend and ask them to pray that you'll listen well and not say anything hurtful.

10. Write down decisions or agreements you make to avoid confusion in the future.

# NOTES

# Session 8

# RESENTMENT

# RESENTMENT

**Definition**

Resentment is "a feeling of indignant displeasure or persistent ill will at something regarded as a wrong, insult, or injury" (merriam-webster.com). An emotion of deep anger or bitterness as a result of being wronged; angry at having been mistreated or personally offended; betrayal of trust. Cold anger buried within as a result of being hurt.

**How Does Resentment Manifest Itself?**

Resentment will often manifest itself in the following ways:
- Strong, aching emotional turmoil felt whenever a certain person or event is discussed.
- The lack of forgiving; the unwillingness to let go and forget.
- A root of distrust and suspicion when dealing with people or events that caused pain in the past.
- Unresolved grief experienced when finding it difficult to accept a loss.
- A grudge held against a person, or group of people, by whom the person in question feels they've been kept from accomplishing something.
- It can be an emotionally disturbing experience that is repeatedly felt or replayed in the mind.

**Reasons Parents May Feel Resentment Toward Their Child/Children**

- The emotional pain they have caused.
- Loss of time away from work.
- Caring for/helping them has cost us money we didn't have—we now have added debt.
- We feel taken advantage of, used, and rejected.
- Our health has suffered.
- Our marriage has suffered—stress and strain leading to increased conflict.
- Relationships with other children have suffered—increased conflict.
- Loss of reputation—our peers may think less of us.

- Time spent in counseling/psychiatrists/support groups (like this one!) we'd rather spend elsewhere. We resent that we have to take the time to be there.
- Having to raise and care for our grandchildren instead of enjoying retirement.
- Shattered expectations—their peers are moving ahead with their lives (careers, marriage, family) while our child is still dysfunctional and can't even hold down a job.

What could you add to this list?

**A Few Ideas for Coping**

- Keep a journal.
- Talk to someone who will listen well and pray with you.
- Limit the amount of time you allow yourself to think about these things.
- Let go and let God.
- Ultimately, we must forgive. If we hold on to resentment we only hurt ourselves. Christ is our example. Forgive as He forgave us. "Bearing with one another and, if one has a complaint against another, forgiving each other; as the Lord has forgiven you, so you also must forgive" (Colossians 3:13).
- When we hold on to resentment, we only hurt ourselves. Practice forgiveness instead.
- Pray for them and ourselves. "Pray for those who mistreat you" (Luke 6:28).

  Ask God, "Take the resentment out of me. Bless _____ in any and every way that seems best to you."

  As we pray this way our attitude changes and sometimes theirs does too.

- Say encouraging things to them instead of being critical or nagging.
- Read encouraging things that uplift you and give hope.

# NOTES

# Session 9

# LETTING GO

# LETTING GO

Letting go can be difficult. It's similar to detaching, no longer trying to fix or change but entrusting your loved one into God's hands. It's releasing your need to control—recognizing only God has that power.

"Let Go," Author Unknown (words in parentheses indicate our additions)

To let go doesn't mean to stop caring. It means I can't do it for someone else.

To let go is not to cut myself off. It's the realization I can't control another.

To let go is to allow someone to learn from natural consequences.

To let go is to recognize when the outcome is not in my hands.

To let go is not to care for, but to care about.

To let go is not to fix, but to be supportive (by listening, empathizing, and finding ways to show you care without doing too much for them—enabling).

To let go is not to judge, but to allow another to be a human being.

To let go is not to expect (demand) miracles, but to take each day as it comes, and cherish myself in it. (To wrestle with the tension between expecting and believing God can do anything—He is the miracle worker—yet accepting what is.)

To let go is not to criticize or regulate anybody, but to try to become what I dream I can be.

To let go is not to regret the past, but to grow and live for the future. (Not dwell on what has happened—it is what it is; we must accept our new normal. God made us very adaptable. We can do it with His strength. Look ahead with hope.)

To let go is to fear less and love more.

1 Peter 5:7

"Cast all your anxiety on him, because he cares for you".

Psalm 55:21  ESV

"Cast your burden on the Lord and he will sustain you."

Proverbs 3:5–6  NASB

"Trust in the Lord with all your heart and do not lean on your own understanding. In all your ways acknowledge Him, and He will make your paths straight."

We do not let go of our sons and daughters releasing them into nothingness. We release them into the hands of a loving and strong God. We let go to let God do His work of transformation and redemption.

## Serenity Prayer

God grant me the serenity to accept the things I cannot change,

Courage to change the things I can,

And wisdom to know the difference.

# NOTES

# Session 10

# EXPECTATIONS

# EXPECTATIONS

One source of frustration we seldom recognize is expecting too much of others or having expectations of what we feel they ought to be, say, give, or do.

What are some expectations you have of your child?

Have you experienced disappointment or anger toward them lately?

Can these emotions be traced back to expectations you had for their reactions or actions?

**Discussion**

"An expectation is a premeditated resentment." Al-Anon quote

**Remedies**

- When we experience resentment we need to look at our expectations.
- We have the right to choose our own standards of conduct, but we do not have the right to impose them on another person. As parents, we are responsible to teach and model certain standards of behavior to our children, but ultimately they have to choose. We can't choose for them.
- Every person has their own reasons for their behavior, beyond our understanding or control. We might say, "But she knew what I expected," not realizing that it may have been the very reason she rebelled and acted differently.
- If we expect another person to react in a certain way to a given situation, and they fail to meet our expectation, do we have the right to be disappointed or angry? It's good to have high standards, but only if we're prepared to accept disappointing results.
- When we let go of expectations we won't feel resentful. If we can adjust our expectations, we'll no longer set ourselves up for constant disappointment.
- Celebrate every accomplishment, no matter how small, and be grateful for it.

**What Is the Answer?**

"What Is the Answer?" "We'll find peace of mind when we stop expecting and relax into acceptance. Contentment comes from accepting gratefully the good that comes to us, not from raging at life because it's not better. And don't take it personally when you're disappointed. This is by no means resignation, but a realistic acceptance of how things are."

## What We Need to Remember

- We are powerless over _____.

- We cannot change our child, but God can!

- Control is an illusion. We have none. But God is in control!

- Stop expecting (at least lower expectations) and accept what is.

- Becoming more informed about our child's issues (bipolar, self-harm, pornography, addiction, etc.) will also help us know what is realistic to expect.

- Accept gratefully any good that comes to us.

- I too often fail to live up to the expectations of others.

- Be thankful for the smallest things.

- The Serenity Prayer can lead us to contentment.

## Scripture

Philippians 4:12

"I have learned the secret of being content in any and every situation."

Romans 15:7 NLT

"Therefore, accept each other just as Christ accepted you so that God will be given glory."

# NOTES

# Session 11

# GUARDING YOUR MARRIAGE

# GUARDING YOUR MARRIAGE

"Crisis in any form can put a marriage relationship at risk. Many parents fall into the routine of daily combat, which eventually leads to a parting of the ways."

**What Problems Do You Think Having a Rebellious Child Can Cause in a Marriage?**

- Added stress in our lives

- Strain and tension in relationships

- More arguing, disagreements, and conflict

- Increased irritability

- Misunderstanding—male/female differences as well as temperament differences

- Being too consumed by the problem—talking about it all the time

- Overlooked or decreased time for each other

- Blame and criticize one another

- Lack of unity—not being on the same page

- Withdraw from each other—isolation

**What Can We Do to Guard Our Marriage in Times of Crisis?**

- Make time for fun, plan a date night once a week and declare it a "no prodigal zone."

- Take turns being the bad guy.

- Present a united front—never disagree in front of a rebellious child. Resolve differences privately.

- Make your marriage your number one priority, not your child—one day your child will move on and you will be left with each other.

- Memorize and practice these statements: "You may be right." (defuses arguments) "What do you need from me right now?" "I'm not the enemy." (keeps perspective)

- Stop blaming and criticizing each other.

- Forgive mistakes and failures.

- The word divorce is not in your vocabulary. Refuse to consider it as an option.

- Pray together. When needed, agree to allow time for emotions to subside before praying.

- Accept that neither of you were perfect parents.

- Being a good listener, slow to speak, not quick to fix.

- Cultivate a hobby together.

- Be honest and vulnerable with your feelings.

- Be grateful for the calm times.

- Intentionally involve yourselves in marriage building activities. (conferences, seminars, small group studies, reading books together, counseling, etc.)

**Scripture:**

Ecclesiastes 4:9–10
"Two are better than one, because they have a good return for their labor: If either of them falls down, one can help the other up. But pity anyone who falls and has no one to help them up."

1 Corinthians 13:4–8
"Love is patient, love is kind. It does not envy, it does not boast, it is not proud. It does not dishonor others, it is not self-seeking, it is not easily angered, it keeps no record of wrongs. Love does not delight in evil but rejoices with the truth. It always protects, always trusts, and always hopes, always perseveres. Love never fails."

# NOTES

# Session 12

# GUARDING YOUR FAMILY

# GUARDING YOUR FAMILY

**Trouble with Our Other Children**

"Crisis in any form can add stress to family relationships. If we have other children, they can be negatively affected by having a troubled brother or sister. This is our topic for today."

What are some of the problems you know of that can arise in other children in the family?

- Resentment, anger, and jealousy build up.

- We give so much time and attention to our troubled child it takes away from them.

- Financial resources the family might have enjoyed are spent on the rebelling child.

- Vacations, education limitations, extracurricular activities or sports, etc. can cause other children to feel cheated because of how their sibling affected these.

- Anger at how they saw us be hurt by their brother or sister—they tire of their behavior and don't like it. They can become like the older brother in the parable of the prodigal son.

- Depression, sadness, or worry over their sibling's welfare—they may need counseling.

- Caretaking—they begin to feel responsible for their sibling; try to protect or keep secrets to keep them safe or maintain peace in the family.

How does this make you feel?

In what ways has enabling negatively impacted other children in your family?

What have you done to prevent or remedy these problems?

## Suggestions

- Intentionally spend time with other children doing normal, meaningful, and fun things together.

- If they no longer live with you, call, email, text, or Skype with them to stay connected.

- Make extra effort to give your other children lots of positive affirmation. Praise them and compliment them as much as possible for their strengths and the blessing they are to you.

- Make time to do special things with and for your other children. Save to give them a special surprise or vacation of their choosing.

- If possible, arrange a family counseling time. Give opportunities for them to express their feelings; family sessions can be therapeutic and healing.

## Scripture

Luke 15:22–32

Parable of the Lost Son

"But the father said to his servants, 'Quick! Bring the best robe and put it on him. Put a ring on his finger and sandals on his feet. Bring the fattened calf and kill it. Let's have a feast and celebrate. For this son of mine was dead and is alive again; he was lost and is found.' So they began to celebrate. Meanwhile, the older son was in the field. When he came near the house, he heard music and dancing. So he called one of the servants and asked what was going on. 'Your brother has come,' he replied, 'and your father has killed the fattened calf because he has him back safe and sound.'

The older brother became angry and refused to go in. So his father went out and pleaded with him. But he answered his father, 'Look! All these years I've been slaving for you and never disobeyed your orders. Yet you never gave me even a young goat so that I could celebrate with my friends. But when this son of yours who has squandered your property with prostitutes comes home, you kill the fattened calf for him!'

'My son,' the father said, 'you are always with me, and everything I have is yours. But we had to celebrate and be glad, because this brother of yours was dead and is alive; he was lost and is found.' "

Ephesians 6:4

"Fathers, do not exasperate your children; instead, bring them up in the training and instruction of the Lord."

# NOTES

# Session 13

# POWERLESSNESS AND CONTROL

# POWERLESSNESS AND CONTROL

## Introduction

What do you have control over in your life?

How do you respond to having no control?

How does that make you feel?

## Three Concepts

I am not the cause of my child's problems.

Ultimately, I can't control my child's problems.

I don't have the power to fix my child's problems.

• It's not your fault, unless you encouraged your child's behavior and aided in their destruction. Stop trying to control. You'll drive yourself crazy and them too. You can't fix them—they have to want to change. You can't force it. Remember, control is an illusion. The only thing we really have control over is ourselves. There's nothing you can do to speed up the healing process, but God is still in control.

• As parents we seek help as a last resort. We find it difficult to surrender to the idea that we, who are usually competent, don't really know how to handle this correctly. Our natural impulse is to take over. This only causes trouble. We have to let go and let God.

• If we really accept the fact that we have no authority or power over another person, then we will not try to force them to do what we want them to do. Admitting our powerlessness is by no means a statement of despair. It helps us accept our limitations and keeps us humble, so that we can find answers that will place our lives on a different course. It prepares us for deliverance from problems we can't cope with alone.

# DECLARATION OF RELEASE

Make this declaration of release[2] as often as necessary:

Because Jesus Christ is my Lord, I free you from my anxiety, fears, and control. I trust the Holy Spirit to lead you and show you the way that is right for you—the way of love, joy, and peace and all that salvation includes.

I place you at God's throne of grace. I cannot force my will on you. I cannot live your life for you. I give you to God the Father, Son, and Holy Spirit. You are a very special person. As much as I love you, God loves you more. Your life today is totally in His hands, and I trust Him with it.

In Jesus' name

I release you from my expectations,

I place you on open palms to the Lord,

I give you my blessings,

I let you go.

In His love,


Signed_____


Date _____


"It is God who works in you to will and to act according to his good purpose; being confident of this, that he who began a good work in you will carry it on to completion until the day of Christ Jesus" (Philippians 2:13, 1:6).

[2] Used with permission from @Sylvia Gunter, The Father's Business, P. O. Box 380333, Birmingham, AL 35238 www.thefathersbusiness.com. Email: info@thefathersbusiness.com

# NOTES

# Session 14

# COMMUNICATION

# COMMUNICATION

**What is the Purpose of Communication**

- To share information
- To express needs
- To get to know others better

**Two Roles of Communication: Talking and Listening**

**What are the qualities of a good talker and a good listener?**

| TALKER | LISTENER |
|---|---|
| Look at the listener | Look at the talker |
| Speak loudly enough | Do not interrupt |
| Speak clearly | Ask questions |
| Use more than one tone of voice | Repeat back what you hear |
| Don't go on and on | Look interested |
| Think about what you want to say | Care about what the talker is saying |
| Use words the listener will understand | Don't talk when the talker is sharing |

**Why are people not good listeners or talkers?**

| TALKER | LISTENER |
|---|---|
| Fear | Anger |
| Shy | Bored |
| Have nothing to say | Tired |
| As a child learned not to talk | Too Busy |

Uncertain how to express thoughts          Distracted

                                           Cannot hear

                                           Under influence

## Techniques for Good Communication

- Give your undivided attention – stop what you're doing, set another time to talk, and respect the time set to talk.
- Take your time—speak slowly, breathe, plan ahead, and sit down.
- Use "I" messages: "I feel _____ when you _____ because _____". This is a good model.
- Speak respectfully—avoid name-calling, yelling, or cursing.
- Allow everyone to have their own feelings, regardless of what they are.
- Verbally recognize both of your feelings and those of the other person – we feel better knowing someone recognizes how we feel, even if they do not agree with us. Heart feelings such as: mad, sad, glad and scared.
- Listen to the person speaking—don't think about what your response will be, and say back what you think you have heard.
- Ask for what you want—don't make demands.
- Remember to show appreciation to the person for their time and effort—don't take this time for granted especially with family members and close friends.

## Scriptures

James 1:19

"My dear brothers and sisters, take note of this: Everyone should be quick to listen, slow to speak and slow to become angry."

Ephesians 4:15  NLT

"Instead, we will speak the truth in love, growing in every way more and more like Christ, who is the head of his body, the church."

# COMMUNICATION WORKSHEET

Learning healthy communication is vital. Complete this form stating positive and negative to the person you will be communicating with, using honesty and feeling words.

1. I feel/felt _____ and _____
when _____.

2. I feel/felt _____ and _____
when _____.

3. I feel/felt _____ and _____
when _____.

4. I feel/felt _____ and _____
when _____.

5. I feel/felt _____ and _____
when _____.

6. I feel/felt _____ and _____
when _____.

7. I feel/felt _____ and _____
when _____.

8. I feel/felt _____ and _____
when _____.

9. I feel/felt _____ and _____
when _____.

10. I feel/felt _____ and _____
when _____.

# NOTES

# Session 15

# WAITING

# WAITING

## Definition

To remain inactive or in a state of repose, as until something expected happens; to look forward to eagerly" (dictionary.com).

## Looking Deeper at Waiting

Waiting is hard work. It takes a lot of concentrated effort and a special kind of self-discipline. Today, waiting goes against everything our culture emphasizes. The problem is, "it took time for our children to get themselves into trouble, and getting . . . out of trouble will probably take time as well".[3]

## Consequences of Not Waiting

What are some of the consequences you can think of that come from not waiting or not waiting well?

## Waiting Well

Waiting is often part of life and our spiritual life is no different. God places us in positions to wait on Him and asks us to do it with patience and expectation of His work in our lives. It helps us focus on who is ultimately in control. We grow in our faith and trust in God. It's okay to tell Him you're exhausted and don't like it. It gives opportunities to develop patience.

## Scriptures

Psalm 27:14
"Wait for the LORD; be strong and take heart and wait for the Lord."

Psalm 130:5
"I wait for the LORD, my whole being waits, and in his word I put my hope."

Psalm 37:7

"Be still before the LORD . . . wait patiently for him; . . . do not fret . . ."

Romans 8:25

"But if we hope for what we do not yet have, we wait for it patiently."

**Five Tips for Waiting**

- Be more focused on God.

- Remember who God is and what He can do.

- Continue to live your life, be active with work, friends, community, etc.

- Take one day at a time, live in the present.

- Remember the promises of God. Get someone else's perspective.

- Keep the big picture in mind. God is developing something in us.

- Remind yourself of God's goodness.

[3] Brendan O'Rourke and DeEtte Sauer, *The Hope of a Homecoming* (Colorado Springs: NavPress, 2003), 117.

# NOTES

# Session 16

# SURVIVING THE HOLIDAYS

# SURVIVING THE HOLIDAYS

**Tips for Surviving the Holidays**

**Tip #1: Adjust or lower your expectations.**

Sometimes we don't realize the expectations we have until they go unfulfilled. Feelings of disappointment, frustration, hurt, anger, and resentment alert us that we had an expectation our child did not meet.

"Expectations are premeditated resentments" according to Al-Anon. When we hold an expectation that isn't met we feel disappointed and hurt. Disappointment and hurt can turn into anger. Anger, over time, results in resentment.

If you can adjust your expectations it will protect your fragile emotions. You can avoid becoming disappointed, hurt, angry, or resentful. Let go of how you wish things would be. Have no expectations of your child's participation or involvement. Then, if things work out the way you wanted, great! You'll be pleasantly surprised.

Matthew 6:10
"Your kingdom come, your will be done . . ."

Ephesians 4:32 NASB
"Be kind to one another, tender-hearted, forgiving each other, just as God in Christ also has forgiven you."

**Tip #2: Consider doing things differently.**

Relevant to the upcoming holiday, what are some traditions that are special to you?

Maybe your former traditions will make you feel worse or be too difficult to do in light of your situation with your son or daughter. If you always cooked a big meal, you could go to a restaurant or to someone else's house instead. If you opened gifts at night, then change it up and open them in the morning.

Isaiah 43:18–19

"Forget the former things, do not dwell on the past; see I am doing a new thing!"

**Tip #3: Focus on others.**

Look for a way to help someone else who has a need. Do something kind for them. You don't have to look too far to find hurting or lonely people. It could be as simple as sending them a card, visiting, or calling them. You could take them out for coffee or a meal; give a box of candy, flowers, or a gift card. Be creative. Mow a lawn, pick up some groceries or fix something around the house. Focusing on someone else takes your attention off yourself and lightens the burden you are carrying. Doing it anonymously would be extra fun.

Philippians 2:4 NASB

"Do not merely look out for your own personal interests, but also for the interests of others."

**Tip #4: Be grateful.**

Keep giving thanks no matter how you feel. Start a thanksgiving journal or a gratitude list. Write down at least one thing in it every day. Don't include only big things: a job, a promotion at work, a new car, etc. Notice little things too—birds singing, the wonder and beauty of nature, a smell of something you like (food cooking on a grill, flowers), friendship, eating something delicious, etc.

What are you grateful for right now?

Ephesians 5:20

"Always giving thanks to God the Father for everything, in the name of our Lord Jesus Christ."

I Thessalonians 5:18

"Give thanks in all circumstances; for this is God's will for you in Christ Jesus."

# NOTES

# Session 17

# COURAGEOUS LOVE

# COURAGEOUS LOVE

Courageous love teaches us to face the crisis, take a stand, and meet challenges. This type of love will help us develop new strengths so we can give a sense of direction and support.

**Agree or Disagree?**

1. Love means never having to say you're sorry.

2. I will always bail my son out of jail.

3. I have to tell my daughter (who's over 18) to move out of my home for not living by my rules. It's the most loving thing I can do.

4. I refuse to call in sick for my son when he can't get up and go to work due to a hangover or staying out too late.

5. It's showing love to step in and make sure they don't fail a class or lose their job.

6. Because we love our child, we took out a second mortgage on our home to pay for their fourth rehab. It's the right thing to do to show them we believe in them.

7. I refuse to drain my savings account or retirement plan to pay my daughter's bills. I'll let her experience the consequences.

8. I will write an excuse for my son's absence from school, even though he didn't have a valid reason.

9. I covered my child with a blanket on the front lawn when they passed out drunk. I left them there. I didn't drag them into the house or put them to bed.

10. I forgave a debt my daughter owed me because I knew she could never pay me back.

11. I will pay for my child's cell phone so I can have contact with them.

12. After my child moves out, I will buy them a meal once a month (or have them over for one), but I won't give them any money or gift cards.

13. I keep telling my son what he should do. If I don't, he'll forget.

14. I refuse to have a relationship with my gay child's partner. It goes against my beliefs.

**Show them Christ**. He is what they really need above all else. It's not an excuse to nag or preach. This often has the opposite effect. Our behavior and attitudes can speak more than words. Christ is our motivation to continue loving even when they don't deserve it.

**Pray**. Only God can change them. Ask others to be part of a prayer team to pray for them and their friends. Email specific requests each week—be sure to include how they can pray for you. Prayer is a powerful way to show our love.

**Tell them.** Even when our children are rebellious, they need to hear that we still love them and see our love in action. When things are at their worst, we're still called to love. When we reach out we might be rejected, but we can't stop. Speak it, text it, email it; do all you can to stay connected. However, don't let them trample on you or not pay the consequences for their destructive choices. Love is not a doormat.

**Keep a journal**. If you don't know where they are or have no way of communicating, you could start keeping a journal. Record things you and the family are doing, things you think would be of interest to them. It could be daily or weekly. Include an expression of love to them with each entry. When they come "home," give them the journal. It might open the door to help rebuild your relationship.

**Welcome them home**. Let them know when they're ready to change your door is always open. You'll be there with open arms to help, encourage, and support them. But don't create too many requirements for returning that could lessen the chances of them coming home.

**Listen**. Another powerful way of showing love is by simply listening. Look for opportunities to just sit with them (maybe on the phone) and listen. Even if they're drunk or high, being there speaks volumes: "Tell me more about that. Tell me what you're feeling. I love you. I care." Be persistent. Don't give up. Once they realize how much you care, it can make all the difference.

**Respect their friends**. Even if you don't like their friends, be kind, thoughtful, and courteous the way you would to any unbeliever. Remember, their friends are someone else's wayward children too. Your son or daughter will take notice of this. You never know the affect it may have later on.

**Take an interest in what they like**. Learn about it so you can ask good questions. Validate those things. Encourage them in these pursuits.

**Be strong.** When you have to correct or discipline (under age 18) always end with, "We love you too much not to do anything about this."

**When asked for money or help that would be enabling say,** "Because we love you, we're not going to step in and take away your privilege of figuring this out on your own. We're confident you can do it and we'll pray for you." Instead, invite them over for a meal or meet at a restaurant or a coffee shop.

**When they've failed in some way, experienced something traumatic, or relapsed say,** "There's nothing you could ever do—or could be done to you—that would ever make me love you any less or any more than I always have. My love for you will never change."

**Keep boundaries.** Love needs healthy boundaries to thrive and protect both parties. Neither should take advantage of the other, nor do anything that's not in the best interest of each person. Sometimes the loving thing to do is the hardest thing to do.

## A True Story

When one couple's son was incarcerated in a state prison for six years, the immediate and extended family (including close friends) agreed to take turns accepting a weekly collect phone call from him so they could stay connected and let him know they still cared. His parents visited weekly and when they couldn't go, another family member or friend went in their place. They gave him clear ultimatums and accepted no excuses. They were willing to go so far, but he had to do his part. They let him know, in no uncertain terms, that they would support him and help him this one time and that would be it. He knew they meant what they said. When he got out of prison, he had a better understanding of their love for him, and how far they were willing to go in order to show it. But he also better understood the boundaries they were setting within that love. Today, twenty years later, he says their courageous love made the difference and changed the course of his life.

**Scripture**

Romans 5:8 ESV

"God shows his love for us in that while we were still sinners, Christ died for us."

1 Corinthians 13:4–8 ESV

"Love is patient and kind; love does not envy or boast; it is not arrogant or rude. It does not insist on its own way; it is not irritable or resentful; it does not rejoice at wrongdoing, but rejoices with the truth. Love bears all things, believes all things, hopes all things, endures all things. Love never ends."

Psalm 118:1

"Give thanks to the LORD, for he is good; his love endures forever."

# NOTES

# Session 18

# FORGIVENESS

# FORGIVENESS

## Definition

"How do you define forgiveness?"

- Forgiveness is not just for the person who needs to be forgiven. It also benefits us, the "forgiver."

- Forgiveness doesn't make the other person right; it makes you free (Al-Anon).

- Forgiveness isn't condoning or excusing the actions or behaviors of others. It's releasing that person to God to let Him deal with them, so we can be set free. For parents in pain, it's part of the process of gaining back our lives.

Some of our children don't even remember or know they need forgiving. Therefore, one reason to forgive is for our own sake and for our own health.

"If we hold on to our anger, we stop growing and our souls begin to shrivel." — M. Scott Peck

Our child may have made decisions and choices that hurt us and cost us a lot: loss of health, sleep, time at work, or finances spent trying to help them or ourselves; loss of or damaged relationships—with them, our spouse, other children, other family members and even friends; loss of our mental and emotional well-being. Our faith can be weakened; we may even walk away from God in disappointment and confusion.

## Five Areas of Forgiveness

1. Forgive our child—for hurting us. We may feel very angry and resentful over how we've been treated. They lied to us, stole from us; told us they hated us, we ruined their lives, and they wanted to get away from us. They broke our hearts and shattered our dreams. We don't trust them, can't believe them, don't even know them anymore. We also feel angry at what they're doing to themselves. The list goes on and on. We must forgive, even if they don't ask us to. Jesus said, "Forgive and you will be forgiven" (Luke 6:37).

2. Forgive ourselves—for not being the perfect parent. There isn't one. Even though we did our best, we still tend to feel a lot of guilt over any part we may have played. Be easy on yourself. Refuse the lie that it's your fault. You didn't make them do any of this. You did the best you could. No matter how badly you may have blown it, it doesn't excuse their choices.

   If we don't forgive ourselves, we'll end up living under the weight of guilt, blame, shame, and a host of other feelings that God never intended. He gave our children a free will to make their own decisions. Don't forget what happened in the Garden of Eden to the only perfect parent (Genesis 2).

3. Forgive others—for hurting our child. This includes those who influenced them negatively, encouraged their destructive choices, sold or gave them drugs, exposed them to pornography, took advantage of them, or didn't help them when they could have. Our friends may hurt us or walk away. They can't handle our pain. They want to, but they can't. It's not their fault. They can't understand what we're going through.

4. Forgive God—sounds strange, doesn't it? It can be very difficult to accept that while God is sovereign and all-powerful, and could have prevented these things, He gave them free will to choose for themselves. Sometimes we blame Him for not protecting them, even though they simply experienced the natural consequences of their choices. Of course He doesn't need to be forgiven. He didn't do anything wrong. In reality, we may need to be forgiven if we've begun to blame Him, allowing resentment to build up in our hearts—maybe without even realizing it. The important thing is to be honest. Tell Him what we're feeling, even if we're angry. It's okay. He understands.

5. Ask forgiveness from our adult children—for mistakes we made. We may or may not have known God and His ways in the years we were raising them. Most of us made at least a few mistakes. Asking their forgiveness brings relief and healing. If God reveals a time when we unintentionally hurt our child—too harsh, too lenient, or enabled—asking forgiveness can have huge benefits for our relationship.

Allison Bottke says, "Though very hard, (it) may be the healing balm needed to prepare them for a spiritual growth spurt. Then again, it could be like pouring lighter fluid on an open flame. You don't know until you try."[4]

Louise Smedes said it so well: "The first and only person to be healed by forgiveness is the person who does the forgiveness. . . . When we genuinely forgive, we set a prisoner free and then discover that the prisoner we set free was us."

## Consequences of Not Forgiving

We need to offer and receive forgiveness. If we don't, it will lead to bitterness, resentment, and cynicism. Forgiveness is the only way to lance the wounds of our heart before they begin to fester and make us sick. Jesus is our role model. We forgive out of obedience to Him because He forgave us. He is the how and the why of forgiving. It's a long, slow process, but if we choose to do it, we can be set free.

Ephesians 4:32
"Be kind and compassionate to each other, forgiving each other, just as in Christ God forgave you."

[4] Allison Bottke, *Setting Boundaries with Your Adult Children* (Eugene, OR: Harvest House, 2008), chapter 5

# NOTES

# Session 19

# THANKFULNESS

# THANKFULNESS

"Give thanks in all circumstances; for this is the will of God in Christ Jesus for you" (1 Thessalonians 5:18).

This Bible passage tells us to be thankful no matter what is happening in our lives. This is what God wants us to do. It's hard when we're going through painful experiences. However, with dependence on God and practice, we can learn to give thanks anyway. By giving thanks we refocus our attention on positive things, lighten our burdens, and increase our awareness of God's activity in our lives.

## Definition

Thankfulness—to express gratitude for something or to someone, usually by saying, "Thank you"; a feeling of appreciation for kindness or thoughtfulness.

## Thoughts on Thankfulness

Researchers with The Gratitude and Thankfulness Project in 2003 found that people who keep gratitude journals on a weekly basis exercised more frequently, reported fewer physical symptoms, felt better about their lives as a whole, and were more optimistic about the upcoming week compared to those who recorded hassles or neutral life events.

When things go wrong and life is hard, God wants us to trust Him. When life is out of control, look for something to be thankful for. Gratitude in hard times is a supernatural response. It's unnatural, but it has the power to lift us up above our circumstances. Our knee-jerk response is to grumble and complain. Pretty soon we begin to feel sorry for ourselves and start having a big pity party. Before we know it, we've turned into a critical, cynical, pessimistic person.

A negative, complaining spirit only hurts us and others in our lives. We aren't very pleasant to be around. People begin to avoid us. What we need to do is reaffirm our trust in God and shift our focus. When we do this, our pessimistic attitude begins to reverse, regardless of how we feel.

Give thanks to God even though it's the opposite of what you want to do. It sounds crazy, but if you at least try, you'll slowly begin to come out of the fog of negativism. You'll begin moving toward a more peaceful place. It is possible.

Thankfulness is a key to uplift the troubled heart. "Do not be anxious about anything, but in every situation, by prayer and petition, with thanksgiving, present your requests to God. And the peace of God, which transcends all understanding, will guard your hearts and your minds in Christ Jesus" (Philippians 4:6–7).

**Start a Gratitude Journal—record at least one thing every day!**

# I'M THANKFUL FOR.....

# NOTES

# Session 20

# SELF-CARE

# SELF-CARE

When we're consumed with our children and their troubles, we tend to neglect our own well-being. Sometimes we become martyrs as we try to save them. This creates huge amounts of stress that will ultimately take a toll on us. If we don't make the effort to take better care of ourselves, then we may end up sick—emotionally, physically, or spiritually. We need to be intentional about our self-care.

**Ways We Are affected**

- We can't sleep or we sleep too much.
- We can't eat or we eat too much.
- We watch a lot of television.
- We become depressed and lethargic. It's difficult to get up in the morning, keep moving, and go to work.
- We withdraw and isolate.
- We don't care about our appearance.
- We experience more physical ailments.
- We're full of anxiety and can't stop worrying. We obsess over our child's behavior.
- We become disillusioned, stop going to church, maybe stop praying—even believing. "Why bother. It hasn't made any difference."
- We doubt God's goodness. "If He's so good, why did He let this happen?"
- Our relationships suffer under the strain: spouse, other children, relatives, and friends.
- We have difficulty concentrating and focusing at work. Our productivity suffers.

**Self-Care Activities**

- Get plenty of rest—nap if you feel the need.

- Eat healthy. Watch your sugar, fat, and caffeine intake. Drink more water. Eat more fresh fruits and vegetables. Don't skip meals. Protein and fiber are good sources of energy.

- Make yourself exercise—at least take a fifteen-minute walk several times a week. Ask a friend to join you or find a group. Exercise releases endorphins in the brain, a natural mood lifter.

- Talk to a counselor, therapist, or clergyperson.

- Find a way to connect with God— reading the Bible, prayer, worship, etc. If this is hard and concentration is lacking, try these approaches: listen to music, appreciate nature, listen to an audio Bible through an app on your electronic device, or read prayers from books written especially for hurting parents.

- Make an appointment with your doctor for a physical if you have persistent physical symptoms.

- Get involved in a support group.

- Simplify your life. Cut back on as many nonessential activities as possible. You need all your reserves to cope with the circumstances.

- Reach out to a few trusted, nonjudgmental friends. Share honestly with them. No more hiding or stuffing your feelings. Secrets make us sick. Limit the amount of time you allow yourself to talk about your child. Too much is counter-productive.

- Enjoy a hobby or cultivate a new one. It's a positive distraction.

- Make time for fun. Do what refreshes you.

"He gives strength to the weary and increases the power of the weak" (Isaiah 40:29).

# NOTES

# Session 21

# HOPE

# HOPE

## Definition

"A feeling of expectation and desire for a certain thing to happen; a feeling of trust (dictionary.com)"; wanting something to come true in the future; to anticipate, look for or desire something or someone.

## Firm and Fragile Hope

- God loves and cares more about our child than we do and will never stop seeking them.
- God is my ally not my adversary.
- I trained my child in the faith and they will return to it someday.
- One day my child will be free from their addiction, mental health issues, self-injury, etc.
- I am not alone. God promised never to leave me or forsake me.
- If I believe and pray earnestly, then my child won't experience negative or lifelong consequences.

Firm hope needs to be in who God is and what He has done for us in Christ. He will be with us; He will help us, and will use all our pain to make us more like his Son. This is His ultimate goal. Firm hope is also in the promises of God, in what He says He will do for us in His Word. Hope is real. God can do the impossible. He transforms lives every day. But there is a tension here—another person's free will is involved. We have no control over what they choose. Our challenge is not to hold too tightly to the hopes we have for our child because this is a fragile hope. Keep trusting for the impossible, but open your hand to receive from God whatever He allows.

We want to be able to say, like the three men of God who were about to be thrown into a fiery furnace: "If we are thrown into the blazing furnace, the God we serve is able to deliver us from it, and he will deliver us from your hand your Majesty. But even if he does not, we want you to know, your Majesty, that we will not serve your gods or worship the image of gold you have set up." (Daniel 3:17–18).

Our goal is to affirm, "even if he does not . . ." "Even if my child never changes in my lifetime, or at all, I will still trust You, Lord.

## Hope Quotes

"We're not necessarily doubting that God will do what's best for us; we are wondering how painful the best will turn out to be." — C.S. Lewis

"Our hope should not be in anyone's behavior or the timing of our struggles." — Mark Gregston

"Our hope is in God alone. We trust him with the what, the how, and the when of the working out of His plan." — Dena Yohe

"Hope is the certainty that God cares for our children more than we do and will never stop seeking them." — Dena Yohe

"We must accept finite disappointment, but never lose infinite hope." — Martin Luther King Jr.

"There is no medicine like hope, no incentive so great, no tonic so powerful as expectations of something better tomorrow." — Dietrich Bonhoeffer

## Hope Activity

An acrostic for hope is – **H**olding **O**n to **P**romises **E**xpectantly.

There are over seven thousand promises in the Bible. Learning many of them will help us build a firm hope we can count on.

*Refer to the "Promises to Claim" in the Appendix.

# NOTES

# Session 22

# RESILIENCE

# RESILIENCE

## Definition

The capacity to recover quickly from difficulties; elasticity; able to bounce back, adapt, and change when stretched.

## Discussion Questions

In what ways have you felt stretched or bent out of shape?

Is this a quality you think we need? Why or why not?

If we're stretched too far we'll break. Do you have a breaking point? What is it?

## How Can We Become Resilient?

1.  Maintain emotional health—not allow emotional, physical, or verbal abuse.

2.  Maintain physical health—good diet, adequate rest, manage medical needs, exercise regularly; exercise releases endorphins and naturally improves a sense of well-being.

3.  Know and be confident about our true identity—who we are (a child of God) and who we belong to (God).

4.  Distinguish between truth and lies; focus on the positive; avoid negative, critical thinking.

5.  Know our eternal destiny—heaven; with God forever.

6.  Be part of a community—a reliable support system; strong friendships with trustworthy, caring, nonjudgmental people; church, Bible studies, support groups.

7.  Know our limits and enforce wise boundaries; no enabling or over helping; know when to say "no" and not give in.

8.  Refuse to isolate in times of crisis and distress; willing to let others know when we're in need; share our struggles with openness and authenticity.

9. Cultivate or pursue a hobby: music, art, reading, gardening, sports (fishing, boating, golf, bowling, swimming, walking, hiking, biking, billiards, tennis, etc.), crafts or sewing, pets, photography, woodworking, etc.

10. Know yourself well; able to identify feelings and take opportunities to talk about them honestly with a friend, clergy, life coach, counselor, or in a small group/support group setting.

11. Cultivate a strong faith in God; grow in the relationship.

12. Develop a thankful disposition—an attitude of gratitude. Make a list and add to it daily. Helps develop contentment and even joy in the midst of trials.

13. Make time for fun—laughter is good medicine.

14. Do whatever refreshes you for the pure enjoyment of it.

**Scripture**

Romans 15:4
"For everything that was written in the past was written to teach us, so that through the endurance taught in the Scriptures and the encouragement they provide we might have hope."

James 5:11 NASB
"We count those blessed who endured."

Hebrews 12:3
"Consider him who endured such opposition from sinners, so that you will not grow weary and lose heart."

2 Corinthians 4:16
"Therefore we do not lose heart. Though outwardly we are wasting away, yet inwardly we are being renewed day by day."

2 Corinthians 4:8–9 ESV
"We are afflicted in every way, but not crushed; perplexed, but not driven to despair; persecuted, but not forsaken; struck down, but not destroyed."

Galatians 6:9 NASB

"Let us not lose heart in doing good, for in due time we will reap if we do not grow weary."

## Reflection

The opposite of resilience is rigid, hardened or defeated. Has your journey had this effect on you? We may need resilience more than we thought. Take a few quiet minutes to talk to God. Ask Him to help you become more resilient.

# NOTES

# Appendix

# THE SERENITY PRAYER

GOD, grant me the serenity

To accept the things I cannot change;

Courage to change the things I can;

And wisdom to know the difference.


Living one day at a time;

Enjoying one moment at a time;

Accepting hardships as the pathway to peace;

Taking, as He did, this sinful world as it is

Not as I would have it;


Trusting that he will make all things right

If I surrender to his will;

That I will be reasonably happy in this life;

And supremely happy with him

Forever in the next.

Amen.

-Reinhold Niebhur


# THE LORD'S PRAYER

Our Father who is in heaven, hallowed be Your name.

Your kingdom come, Your will be done, on earth as it is in heaven.

Give us this day our daily bread. And forgive us our debts, as we also have forgiven our debtors.

And do not lead us into temptation, but deliver us from evil.

For Yours is the kingdom and the power and the glory forever. Amen.

# I BLESS YOU PRAYER

I bless you with unwavering hope.

Romans 15:13

*"May the God of hope fill you with all joy and peace*
*As you trust in Him,*
*So that you may overflow with hope,*
*By the power of the Holy Spirit."*

I bless you with unshakable faith, so that no matter what happens, you're convinced God will be with you.

I bless you with unspeakable joy that defies reason.

I bless you with unfaltering peace in every circumstance, because you know the Living God is your constant companion.

I bless you with the unthinkable, supernatural ability to trust, no matter what you see happening.

I bless you with unimaginable, divine strength that far surpasses your own, sufficient to carry you through anything and everything that should ever come your way.

I bless you with an unusual outpouring of the Holy Spirit, so that by His unlimited power, the "God of hope" will give you abundant joy, peace, hope, and strength as you walk this difficult path with your child.

I bless you in the beautiful name of Jesus.

Amen.

Dena Yohe  2013

# DECLARATION OF RELEASE

We are selfish by nature. Nobody had to teach us to want things our way. When someone doesn't do things our way, we try to change them, to make them conform to what we believe is right and best. We may feel that someone is heading in the wrong direction, and we want to get him on the track we believe to be right. We may call it concern, but it really may be selfishness and control. No matter how right we may be, we are wrong to try to control others and make them conform to our desires, even our godly desires. It is God's job to change people, not ours. Be careful of trying to control others. Give them to God so He can accomplish His perfect will in their lives.

Make this declaration of release2 as often as necessary:

Because Jesus Christ is my Lord, I free you from my anxiety, fears, and control. I trust the Holy Spirit to lead you and show you the way that is right for you—the way of love, joy, and peace and all that salvation includes.

I place you at God's throne of grace. I cannot force my will on you. I cannot live your life for you. I give you to God the Father, Son, and Holy Spirit. You are a very special person. As much as I love you, God loves you more. Your life today is totally in His hands, and I trust Him with it.

to In Jesus' name

I release you from my expectations,

I place you on open palms to the Lord,

I give you my blessings,

I let you go.

In His love,

Signed_____

Date _____

*"It is God who works in you to will and to act according to his good purpose; being confident of this, that he who began a good work in you will carry it on to completion until the day of Christ Jesus"* (Philippians 2:13, 1:6).

2 Used with permission from @Sylvia Gunter, The Father's Business, P. O. Box 380333, Birmingham, AL 35238 www.thefathersbusiness.com. Email: info@thefathersbusiness.com

# EIGHT TRUTHS FOR YOUR HEART

Is fear ruling your life too much? When you really think about it are you afraid to say "no", afraid to not help, afraid to show your anger or hurt, afraid to show you're confusion, afraid of the unknowns, of what's next, of not being in control, of having no guarantees?

**<u>Remember these 8 truths for your heart:</u>**

1.  God is in control, even when it doesn't look like it.

2.  You are not alone.

3.  You and your child are in His hands.

4.  No matter what happens you will be okay.

5.  With God's help you can handle anything.

6.  You can reach out to others for help.

7.  You can reach out to God in prayer anytime, anywhere.

8.  You can let go and let God work.

Al-Anon says, "We turn our will and our life over to the care of God . . ." That is exactly what we must keep doing—over and over again.

Psalm 71:2
"Be my rock of refuge to which I can always go..."

# THE REST OF VICTORY

THERE IS NOTHING – NO CIRCUMSTANCE, NO TESTING –

THAT CAN EVER TOUCH ME, UNTIL FIRST OF ALL,

IT HAS GONE PAST GOD AND PAST CHRIST, RIGHT THROUGH TO ME.

IF IT HAS COME THAT FAR, IT HAS COME WITH A GREAT PURPOSE WHICH I MAY

NOT UNDERSTAND AT THE MOMENT.

BUT AS I REFUSE TO BECOME PANICKY,

AS I LIFT UP MY EYES TO HIM AND ACCEPT IT

AS COMING FROM THE THRONE OF GOD

FOR SOME GREAT PURPOSE OR BLESSING TO MY OWN HEART,

NO SORROW WILL EVER DISTURB ME,

NO TRIAL WILL EVER DISARM ME,

NO CIRCUMSTANCE WILL CAUSE ME TO FRET.

FOR I SHALL REST IN THE JOY OF WHAT MY LORD IS.

AND THAT IS THE REST OF VICTORY!

ALAN REDPATH

# PROMISES

❖ *I am not alone. God is with me and will never leave me or forsake me.*

"God has said, 'Never will I leave you; never will I forsake you' " (Hebrews 13:5b).

"The LORD Almighty is with us; the God of Jacob is our fortress" (Psalm 46: 7).

"So do not fear, for I am with you; do not be dismayed, for I am your God. I will strengthen you and help you; I will uphold you with my righteous right hand" (Isaiah 41:10a).

"And teaching them to obey everything I have commanded you. And surely I am with you always, to the very end of the age" (Matthew 28:20).

❖ *God loves me and my child with an unfailing, eternal love.*

"For God so loved the world that he gave his one and only Son, that whoever believes in him shall not perish but have eternal life" (John 3:16).

❖ *I have all the help I need from the Holy Spirit – a Helper, Advocate, Counselor, and Comforter.*

"And I will ask the Father, and he will give you another Counselor to be with you forever" (John 14:16).

"But the Counselor, the Holy Spirit, whom the Father will send in my name, will teach you all things and will remind you of everything I have said to you" (John 14:26).

"When the Counselor comes, whom I will send to you from the Father, the Spirit of truth who goes out from the Father, he will testify about me" (John 15:26).

"But I tell you the truth: It is for your good that I am going away. Unless I go away, the Counselor will not come to you; but if I go, I will send him to you" (John 16:7).

❖ *Jesus prays for me all the time.*

"Therefore he is able to save completely those who come to God through him, because he always lives to intercede for them" (Hebrews 7:25).

❖ *God wants to help my child, will never stop seeking him/her. He does not want them to perish.*

"The Lord is not slow in keeping his promise, as some understand slowness. He is patient with you, not wanting anyone to perish, but everyone to come to repentance" (2 Peter 3:9).

❖ *God is patient and slow to anger with my child.*

"And he passed in front of Moses, proclaiming, 'The LORD, the LORD, the compassionate and gracious God, slow to anger, abounding in love and faithfulness" ' (Exodus 34:6).

"Love is patient, love is kind. It does not envy, it does not boast, it is not proud" (1 Corinthians 13:4).

❖ *God always hears my prayers.*

"The LORD is far from the wicked but he hears the prayer of the righteous" (Proverbs 15:29).

❖ *God will accomplish His purposes in my life.*

"The LORD Almighty has sworn, 'Surely, as I have planned, so it will be, and as I have purp d, so it will stand' " (Isaiah 14: 24).

❖ *God will give me the strength and endurance I need.*

"He gives strength to the weary and increases the power of the weak. Even youths grow tired and weary, and young men stumble and fall" (Isaiah 40:29-30).

❖ *I can be joyful in trails.*

"Though the fig tree does not bud and there are no grapes on the vines, though the olive crop fails and the fields produce no food, though there are no sheep in the pen and no cattle in the stalls, yet I will rejoice in the LORD, I will be joyful in God my Savior. The Sovereign LORD is my strength; he makes my feet like the feet of a deer, he enables me to go on the heights" (Habakkuk 3:17-19).

❖ *I don't need to worry about anything, pray instead to have peace of heart and mind.*

"Do not be anxious about anything, but in everything, by prayer and petition, with thanksgiving, present your requests to God. And the peace of God, which transcends all understanding, will guard your hearts and your minds in Christ Jesus" (Philippians 4:6-7).

❖ *There is purpose for our pain.*

"I wrote as I did so that when I came I should not be distressed by those who ought to make me rejoice. I had confidence in all of you, that you would all share my joy. For I wrote you out of great distress and anguish of heart and with many tears, not to grieve you but to let you know the depth of my love for you" (2 Corinthians 2:3-5).

"But we have this treasure in jars of clay to show that this all-surpassing power is from God and not from us. We are hard pressed on every side, but not crushed; perplexed, but not in despair; persecuted, but not abandoned; struck down, but not destroyed. We always carry around in our body the death of Jesus, so that the life of Jesus may also be revealed in our body" (2 Corinthians 4:7-10).

❖ *There is always hope.*

"This is what the LORD says: 'Restrain your voice from weeping and your eyes from tears, for your work will be rewarded,' declares the LORD. 'They will return from the land of the enemy. So there is hope for your future,' declares the LORD. 'Your children will return to their own land' " (Jeremiah 31:16-17).

"Why are you downcast, O my soul? Why so disturbed within me? Put your hope in God, for I will yet praise him, my Savior and my God" (Psalm 42:5).

"But as for me, I will always have hope; I will praise you more and more. My mouth will tell of your righteousness, of your salvation all day long, though I know not its measure" (Psalm 71:14-15).

❖ *God will lead and guide me.*

"The LORD is my shepherd; I shall not be in want. He makes me lie down in green pastures, he leads me beside quiet waters, he restores my soul. He guides me in paths of righteousness for his name's sake" (Psalm 23:1-3).

"They will neither hunger nor thirst, nor will the desert heat or the sun beat upon them. He who has compassion on them will guide them and lead them beside springs of water" (Isaiah 49:10).

❖ *God will give me wisdom.*

"If any of you lacks wisdom, he should ask God, who gives generously to all without finding fault, and it will be given to him" (James 1:5).

❖ *This pain won't last forever.*

"For I consider that the sufferings of this present time are not worthy to be compared with the glory that is to be revealed to us" (Romans 8:18).

"And I heard a loud voice from the throne saying, "Now the dwelling of God is with men, and he will live with them. They will be his people, and God himself will be with them and be their God. He will wipe every tear from their eyes. There will be no more death or mourning or crying or pain, for the old order of things has passed away" (Revelation 21:3-4).

❖ *God is still good no matter what.*

"How great is your goodness, which you have stored up for those who fear you, which you bestow in the sight of men on those who take refuge in you" (Psalm 31:19 ).

"When you give it to them, they gather it up; when you open your hand, they are satisfied with good things" (Psalm 104:28 ).

"Be at rest once more, O my soul, for the LORD has been good to you" (Psalm 116:7).

❖ *Nothing will ever separate me from the love of God.*

"For I am convinced that neither death nor life, neither angels nor demons, neither the present nor the future, nor any powers, neither height nor depth, nor anything else in all creation, will be able to separate us from the love of God that is in Christ Jesus our Lord" (Romans 8:38-39).

❖ *God cares about my pain. He weeps with me, collects my tears in His bottle; wipes my tears.*

"Cast all your anxiety on him because he cares for you" (1 Peter 5:7).

"Record my lament; list my tears on your scroll - are they not in your record?" (Psalm 56:8).

"And I heard a loud voice from the throne saying, 'Now the dwelling of God is with men, and he will live with them. They will be his people, and God himself will be with them and be their God. He will wipe every tear from their eyes. There will be no more death or mourning or crying or pain, for the old order of things has passed away' " (Revelation 21:3-4).

❖ *I will survive this because the Lord is my help and strength.*

"God is our refuge and strength, an ever-present help in trouble. Therefore we will not fear, though the earth give way and the mountains fall into the heart of the sea . . ." (Psalm 46:1-2).

"So do not fear, for I am with you; do not be dismayed, for I am your God. I will strengthen you and help you; I will uphold you with my righteous right hand" (Isaiah 41:10).

❖ *God is trustworthy and faithful.*

"For great is his love toward us, and the faithfulness of the LORD endures forever. Praise the LORD" (Psalm 117:2).

❖ *God can do the impossible.*

"The disciples were even more amazed, and said to each other, 'Who then can be saved?' Jesus looked at them and said, 'With man this is impossible, but not with God; all things are possible with God' " (Mark 10:26-27).

❖ *God is able to do more than I think or imagine.*

"Now to him who is able to do immeasurably more than all we ask or imagine, according to his power that is at work within us" (Ephesians 3:20).

❖ *God gives sufficient grace each day and His power for our weakness.*

"But he said to me, 'My grace is sufficient for you, for my power is made perfect in weakness.' Therefore I will boast all the more gladly about my weaknesses, so that Christ's power may rest on me. That is why, for Christ's sake, I delight in weaknesses, in insults, in hardships, in persecutions, in difficulties. For when I am weak, then I am strong" (2 Corinthians 12: 9-10).

❖ *God will sustain me through this hard time.*

"Surely God is my help; the Lord is the one who sustains me" (Psalm 54:4).

"Cast your cares on the LORD and he will sustain you; he will never let the righteous fall" (Psalm 55:22).

❖ *God is forgiving and good, abounding in love to all who call on Him.*

"You are forgiving and good, O Lord, abounding in love to all who call to you" (Psalm 86:5).

❖ *Godly sorrow brings repentance that leads to salvation with no regrets.*

"Godly sorrow brings repentance that leads to salvation and leaves no regret, but worldly sorrow brings death" (2 Corinthians 7:10).

❖ *God blesses His people with peace.*

"The LORD gives strength to his people; the LORD blesses his people with peace" (Psalm 29:11).

❖ *When we pray, God will answer.*

"When I called, you answered me; you made me bold and stouthearted" (Psalm 138:3).

❖ *God is close to the brokenhearted and saves those who are crushed in spirit.*

"The LORD is close to the brokenhearted and saves those who are crushed in spirit" (Psalm 34:18).

❖ *God will comfort us in all our troubles.*

"Praise be to the God and Father of our Lord Jesus Christ, the Father of compassion and the God of all comfort, who comforts us in all our troubles, so that we can comfort those in any trouble with the comfort we ourselves have received from God. For just as the sufferings of Christ flow over into our lives, so also through Christ our comfort overflows" (2 Corinthians 1:3-5).

❖ *I can do all that I need to do through the strength of Christ.*

"I can do everything through him who gives me strength" (Philippians 4:13).

❖ *God will restore us again.*

"Though you have made me see troubles, many and bitter, you will restore my life again; from the depths of the earth you will again bring me up. You will increase my honor and comfort me once again" (Psalm 71:20-21).

# RECOMMENDED BOOKS AND RESOURCES

## General Comfort

Barnes, Emily. *My Cup Overflows...with the Comfort of God's Love*. Eugene, OR: Harvest House, 1998.

Coleman, Bill. *Parents with Broken Hearts: Helping Parents of Prodigals to Cope*. Rev. ed. Winona Lake, IN: BMH Books, revised edition, 2007.

Crabb, Larry. *Shattered Dreams: God's Unexpected Pathway to Joy*. Colorado Springs: WaterBrook, 2001.

Dobson, Dr. James. *When God Doesn't Make Sense*. Carol Stream, IL: Tyndale House, 1993.

Dravecky, Dave. *Do Not Lose Heart: Meditations of Encouragement and Comfort*. Grand Rapids: Zondervan, 2001.

Guthrie, Nancy. *Holding on to Hope: A Pathway Through Suffering to the Heart of God*. Wheaton, IL: Tyndale, 2002.

_____. *The One Year Book of Hope*. Wheaton, IL: Tyndale House, 2005.

Kent, Carol. *A New Kind of Normal: Hope-filled Choices When Life Turns Upside Down*. Nashville: Thomas Nelson, 2007.

Kent, Carol. *When I Lay My Isaac Down: Unshakable Faith in Unthinkable Circumstances*. Colorado Springs: NavPress, 2004.

Lucado, Max. *God Will Use This for Good: Surviving the Mess of Life*. Nashville: Thomas Nelson, 2013.

_____. *It's Not About Me: Rescue from the Life We Thought Would Make Us Happy*. Nashville: Integrity, 2004.

Lucas, Jeff. *Will Your Prodigal Come Home? An Honest Discussion of Struggle and Hope*. Grand Rapids: Zondervan, 2007.

O'Rourke, Brendan, and DeEtte Sauer. *The Hope of a Homecoming: Entrusting Your Prodigal to a Sovereign God*. Colorado Springs: Navpress, 2003.

Thompson, Marjorie J., and Stephen D. Bryant. *Companions in Christ: The Way of Forgiveness: Participants Book*. Nashville: Upper Room, 2002.

Tworkowski, Jamie. *If You Feel Too Much: Thoughts on Things Found and Lost and Hoped For*. New York: Jeremy P. Tarcher, 2015.

Voskamp, Ann. *One Thousand Gifts: A Dare to Live Fully Right Where You Are*. Grand Rapids: Zondervan, 2010.

Vujicic, Nick. *Life Without Limits: Inspiration for a Ridiculously Good Life.* Colorado Springs: WaterBrook, 2010.

Walsh, Sheila. *Life is Tough but God is Faithful.* Nashville: Thomas Nelson, 1999.

Warren, Rick. *The Purpose Driven Life: What on Earth Am I Here For?* Grand Rapids: Zondervan, 2002.

Wright, H. Norman. *Experiencing Grief.* Nashville: B&H Publishing Group, 2004.

_____. *Loving a Prodigal: A Survival Guide for Parents of Rebellious Children.* Colorado Springs: Chariot Victor, 1999.

Yohe, Dena. *You Are Not Alone: Hope for Hurting Parents of Troubled Kids.* Colorado Springs: WaterBrook, 2016.

Yohe, Renee. *Purpose for the Pain.* Orlando, FL: Bonded Books, 2008.

**Websites**

Hope For Hurting Parents, www.HopeForHurtingParents.com

# Prayer

Banks, James. *Prayers for Prodigals: 90 Days of Prayer for Your Child.* Grand Rapids: RBC Ministries, 2011.

Berndt, Jodie. *Praying the Scriptures for Your Teenagers: Discover How to Pray God's Will for Their Lives.* Grand Rapids: Zondervan, 2007.

Cosby, Sharron. *Praying for Your Addicted Loved One: 90 in 90.* Auburn, WA: Bookjolt, 2013.

Logan, Jim. *Reclaiming Surrendered Ground: Protecting Your Family from Spiritual Attacks.* Chicago: Moody: 1995.

Morgan, Robert J. *Moments for Families with Prodigals.* Colorado Springs: NavPress, 2003.

Omartian, Stormie. *The Power of a Praying Parent.* Eugene, OR: Harvest House, 2014.

_____. *The Power of Praying for Your Adult Children.* Eugene, OR: Harvest House, 2009.

Roberts, Lee. *Praying God's Will for My Daughter.* Rev. ed. Nashville: Thomas Nelson, 2002.

_____. *Praying God's Will for My Son.* Rev. ed. Nashville: Thomas Nelson, revised 2002.

Thompson, Janet. *Praying for Your Prodigal Daughter: Hope, Help and Encouragement for Hurting Parents.* New York: Howard Books, 2007.

**Websites**

Breakthrough, www.intercessors.org

Prayer for Prodigals, http://prayerforprodigals.com, developed by Cru (formerly Campus Crusade for Christ). Request an invitation via e-mail: prayerforprodigals@gmail.com. This is a password-protected site on which you can post prayer requests and receive prayers back from participants by e-mail. It's full of resources: Scripture verses, prayers, recommended books, inspirational devotionals, and places for help around the country for many issues (therapeutic boarding schools for teens, drug and alcohol rehabs, wilderness camps for youth, eating disorder programs, and more).

Facebook pages: 365 Days of Prayers for Prodigals; Prayer for Prodigals; and The Prodigal Hope Network.

## Addiction

Alcoholics Anonymous. *The Big Book*. 4th ed. New York: Alcoholics Anonymous World Services, 2001. Available at meetings and online. Brochures available at meetings.

Al-Anon literature. *Courage to Change and One Day at a Time in Al-Anon II*. Available at meetings and online. Brochures available at meetings.

Conyers, Beverly. *Addict in the Family: Stories of Loss, Hope, and Recovery*. Center City, MN: Hazelden, 2003.

_____. *Everything Changes: Help for Families of Newly Recovering Addicts*. Center City, MN: Hazelden, 2009.

Hayden, Karilee and Wendi Hayden English. *Wild Child, Waiting Mom: Finding Hope in the Midst of Heartache*. Wheaton, IL: Tyndale, 2006.

Hersh, Sharon. *The Last Addiction: Why Self-Help if Not Enough, Own Your Desire, Live Beyond Recovery, Find Lasting Freedom*. Colorado Springs; WaterBrook, 2008.

White, John. *Parents in Pain: Overcoming the Hurt and Frustration of Problem Children*. Downers Grove, IL: Intervarsity Press, 1979.

VanVonderen, Jeff. *Hope and Help for the Addicted*. Grand Rapids: Revell, 2004.

Vawter, John, ed. *Hit by a Ton of Bricks*. Little Rock, AR: Family Life Publishing, 2003.

White, John. *Parents in Pain: A Book of Comfort and Counsel*. Downers Grove, IL: InterVarsity, 1979.

## Websites

About Alcoholism, www.aboutalcoholism.org.

Al-Anon Family Groups, www.al-anon.org.

Celebrate Recovery, www.celebraterecovery.com.

Co-Dependents Anonymous; www.coda.org.

Nar-Anon Family Groups, www.nar-anon.org.

## Boundaries

Adams, Jane. *When Our Grown Kids Disappoint Us: Letting Go of Their Problems, Loving Them Anyway, and Getting On with Our Lives.* New York: Free Press, 2003.

Beattie, Melodie. *CoDependent No More: How to Stop Controlling Others and Start Caring for Yourself.* Center City, MN: Hazelden, 1992.

Bottke, Allison. *Setting Boundaries with Your Adult Children.* Eugene, OR: Harvest House, 2008.

Cloud, Henry, and John Townsend. *Boundaries: When to Say Yes, When to Say No to Take Control of Your Life.* Grand Rapids: Zondervan, 1992.

Friends in Recovery. *The Twelve Steps for Christian from Addictive and Other Dysfunctional Families: Based on Biblical Teachings.* San Diego: Recovery Publications, 1988.

Rubin, Charles. *Don't Let Your Kids Kill You: A Survival Guide for Parents of Drug Addicts and Alcoholics.* 3rd ed. Petaluma, CA: NewCentury, 2010.

## For Parents of Troubled Adolescents

Dobson, James. *The New Strong-Willed Child: Birth Through Adolescence.* Wheaton, IL: Tyndale, 2004.

Gregston, Mark. *When Your Teen is Struggling.* Eugene, OR: Harvest House, 2007. See also the website www.heartlightministries.org.

Hersh, Sharon. *Mom, Everyone Else Does! Becoming Your Daughter's Ally in Responding to Peer Pressure to Drink, Smoke, and Use Drugs.* Colorado Springs: WaterBrook, 2005.

_____. *Mom I Feel Fat! Becoming Your Daughter's Ally in Developing a Healthy Body Image.* Colorado Springs: Shaw, 2001.

_____. *Mom Everyone Else Does! Becoming Your Daughter's Ally Through the Emotional Ups and /downs of Adolescence.* Colorado Springs: WaterBrook, 2004.

_____. *Mom, Sex is No Big Deal! Becoming Your Daughter's Ally in Developing a Healthy Sexual Identity.* Colorado Springs: Shaw, 2006.

Jantz, Gregory L. *When Your Teenager Becomes The Stranger in Your House.* Colorado Springs: David C. Cook, 2011.

Scott, Buddy. *Relief for Hurting Parents: What to Do and How to Think When You're Having Trouble with Your Kids.* Nashville: Oliver-Nelson Books, 1989. See also author's website: www.buddyscott.com.

Tripp, David. *Age of Opportunity: A Biblical Guide to Parenting Teens.* Phillipsburg, NJ: P&R Publishing, 1997, 2001. See also author's website: www.paultripp.com.

**Website**

Dr. Dobson's Family Talk, http://drjamesdobson.org.

## Bullying

*Bullying in a Cyber World, Grades 4 to 5.* Rowley, MA: Didax, 2012. Additional materials are available for parents and schools.

*Bullying in a Cyber World, Grades 6 to 8.* (Rowley, MA: Didax, 2012). Additional materials are available for parents and schools.

Gerali, Dr. Steve. *What Do I Do When: Teenagers Encounter Bullying and Violence?* Grand Rapids: Zondervan, 2009.

Mayo Clinic Staff. *"Bullying: Help Your Child Handle a Bully."* August 23, 2013. www.mayoclinic.org/healthy-living/childrens-health/in-depth/bullying/art-20044918?pg=1.

Miller, Cindy, and Cynthia Lowen. *The Essential Guide to Bullying: Prevention and Intervention: Protecting Children and Teens from Physical, Emotional, and Online Bullying.* New York: Alpha Books, 2012.

National Education Association. *Bully Free: It Starts with Me.* The National Education Association (NEA; www.nea.org) program to stop bullying in public schools.

Students Against Being Bullied, SABB Inc., www.studentsagainstbeingbullied.org, offers antibullying programs that can be used in schools.

van der Zande, Irene. *"Face Bullying with Confidence: 8 KidPower Skills We Can Use Right Away."* Santa Cruz, CA: KidPower, 2011.

_____. *Kidpower Solutions.* Santa Cruz, CA: Kidpower, 2010.

## Mental Health

Alcorn, Nancy. *Starved: Mercy for Eating Disorders.* Enumclaw, WA: Winepress Publishing, 2007.

Amador, Xavier. *I Am Not Sick, I Don't Need Help: How to Help Someone with Mental Illness Accept Treatment*. Peconic, NY: VidaPress, 2010. See also the website www.leapinstitute.org.

Bengtson, Michelle. *Hope Prevails: Insights from a Doctor's Personal Journey through Depression*. Grand Rapids: Revell, 2016.

Comer, John Mark. *My Name is Hope: Anxiety, Depression, and Life after Melancholy*. Portland, OR: Graphe, 2011.

Duke, Patty and Gloria Hochman. *A Brilliant Madness: Living with Manic-Depressive Illness*. New York, NY: Bantam, 1992.

Evans, Dwight L., and Linda Wasmer Andrews. *If Your Adolescent Has Depression or Bipolar Disorder: An Essential Resource for Parents*. New York: Oxford University Press, 2006.

Federman, Russ and J. Anderson Thompson, *Facing Bipolar: The Young Adult's Guide to Dealing with Bipolar Disorder*. Oakland, CA: New Harbinger, 2010.

Foa, Edna, and Linda Wasmer Linda Abdrews. *If Your Adolescent Has Depression or Bipolar Disorder: An Essential Resource for Parents*. New York: Oxford University Press, 2006.

Haughton, Debbie. "What Is EMDR and Can It Help My Child?" *Hope for Hurting Parents* (blog). http://HopeforHurtingParents.com/2014/06/18/what-is-emdr-and-can-it-help-my-child.

Hornbacher, Marya. *Wasted: A Memoir of Anorexia and Bulimia*. New York,: HarperCollins, 1999.

Jamison, Kay Redfield. *An Unquiet Mi*nd. New York: Knopf, 1995.

Levine, Jerome, and Irene S. Levine. *Schizophrenia for Dummies*. Hoboken, NJ: Wiley, 2009.

Mason, Paul T. MS and Randi Kreger. *Stop Walking on Eggshells: Taking Your Life Back When Someone You Care About has Borderline Personality Disorder*. Oakland, CA: New Harbinger, 2010.

Mondimore, Francis M. *Bipolar Disorder: A Guide for Patients and Families*. Baltimore: Johns Hopkins University Press, 1999.

Morrow, Jena, *Hope for the Hollow: A Thirty-Day Inside-Out Make-over for Women Recovering from Eating Disorders*. Raleigh, NC: Lighthouse Publishing, 2013.

Mueser, Kim T., and Susan Gingerich. *The Complete Family Guide to Schizophrenia: Helping Your Loved One Get the Most out of Life*. New York: Guilford Press, 2006.

Walsh, Sheila. *Loved Back to Life: How I Found the Courage to Live Free*. Nashville: Thomas Nelson, 2015.

Zayfert, Claudia, and Jason C. DeViva. *When Someone You Love Suffers from Posttraumatic Stress: What to Expect and What You can Do*. New York: Guilford Press, 2011.

### Websites

Bring Change 2 Mind, www.bringchange2mind.org.

International Bipolar Foundation (IBPF), http://ibpf.org.

National Alliance on Mental Illness (NAMI), www.nami.org.

To find a counselor: www.findchristiancounselor.com or www.psychologytoday.com

## Self-Injury (Self-Harm, Self-Mutilation)

Alcorn, Nancy. *Cut.* Enumclaw, WA: Winepress, 2007.

Leatham, Victoria. *Blood Letting: A Memoir of Secrets, Self-Harm, and Survival.* Oakland, CA: New Harbinger, 2006.

Strong, Marilee. *A Bright Red Scream: Self-Mutilation and the Language of Pain.* New York: Viking, 1998.

S.A.F.E. Alternatives (Self Abuse Finally Ends), selfinjury.com; Need help? Call 800-DONTCUT (366-8288) Information line.

### Websites

The Butterfly Project, www.butterfly-project.tumblr.com.

Mercy Multiplied, http://mercymultiplied.com.

SAFE Alternatives (Self Abuse Finally Ends), www.selfinjury.com; information hotline: 800-DONTCUT (366-8288).

Self-Mutilators Anonymous (SMA), www.selfmutilatorsanonymous.org.

## Same-Sex Attraction

Dallas, Joe. *The Gay Gospel? How Pro-Gay Advocates Misread the Bible.* Eugene, OR: Harvest House, 2007.

_____. *When Homosexuality Hits Home: What to Do When a Loved One Says They're Gay.* Eugene, OR: Harvest House, 2004.

Haley, Mike. *101 Frequently Asked Questions About Homosexuality.* Eugene, OR: Harvest House, 2004.

Johnson, Barbara. *When Your Child Breaks Your Heart: Help for Hurting Moms.* Grand Rapids: Baker Publishing, 1979.

Kaltenbach, Caleb. *Messy Grace: How a Pastor with Gay Parents Learned to Love Others Without Sacrificing Conviction.* Colorado Springs: WaterBrook, 2015.

Martin, Andrew. *Love Is an Orientation: Elevating the Conversation with the Gay Community.* Downers Grove, IL: InterVarsity, 2009.

Worthen, Anita and Bob Davies. *Someone I Love is Gay: How Family and Friends Can Respond.* Downers Grove, IL: InterVarsity, 1996.

Yuan, Christopher and Angela Yuan. *Out of a Far Country.* Colorado Springs: WaterBrook, 2011.

**Websites**

Lead Them Home, www.leadthemhome.org

Living Stones Ministries, www.livingstonesministries.org

## Sensory Processing Disorder

Heller, Sharon. *Too Loud, Too Bright, Too Fast, Too Tight: What to Do If You Are Sensory Defensive in an Overstimulating World.* New York: Harper Collins, 2002. See also author's website: www.sharonheller.net.

Kranowitz, Carol. *The Out of Sync Child: Recognizing and Coping with Sensory Processing Disorder.* New York: Penguin, 2005. See also the STAR Center: Sensory Therapies and Research website: www.spdstar.org.

## Sexual Abuse

The Healing Tree. Orange County, FL. http://caccentral.com/the-healing-tree. Search online for sexual assault programs in your county or city to find help for yourself or your child.

Heitritter, Lynn and Jeanette Vough. *Helping Victims of Sexual Abuse.* Minneapolis: Baker, 2006.

Mann, Mary Ellen. *From Pain to Power: Overcoming Sexual Trauma and Reclaiming Your True Identity.* Colorado Springs: WaterBrook, 2015.

Oakley, Diana. *Intended Harm.* Orlando, FL: Legacy Publishing, 2012.

O'Branyll, Fiona. *A Bright New Place: Triumph After Trauma.* Bloomington, IN: Westbow, 2013.

Omartian, Stormie. *Just Enough Light for the Step I'm On.* Eugene, OR: Harvest House, 2008.

Restoring the Heart Ministries (www.rthm.cc). See *In The Wildflowers*, book and support material written by Julie Woodley, a ten-part DVD series focused on recovery from sexual trauma. It was produced in cooperation with the American Association of Christian Counselors (www.aacc.net). Call 1-800-526-8673 for more information.

Victim Service Centers: Search online to find one in your county or for sexual assault hotlines.

## Suicide

Biebel, David B., and Suzanne L. Foster. *Finding Your Way after the Suicide of Someone You Love*. Grand Rapids: Zondervan, 2005.

Fine, Carla. *No Time to Say Goodbye: Surviving the Suicide of a Loved One*. New York: Doubleday, 1997.

Hsu, Albert. *Grieving a Suicide: A Loved One's Search for Comfort, Answers, and Hope*. Downers Grove, IL: InterVarsity, 2002.

Jamison, Kay Redfield. *Night Falls Fast: Understanding Suicide*. New York: Knopf, 1999.

Smolin, Ann, and John Guinan, John. *Healing After the Suicide of a Loved One*. New York: Simon & Schuster, 1993.

**Websites and Hotlines:**

National Suicide Prevention Lifeline 1-800-273-8255 (TALK). Call 24/7 365 days a year, including holidays, www.suicidepreventionlifeline.org.

American Foundation of Suicide Prevention, www.afsp.org.

QPR Institute, www.qprinstitute.com. Offers suicide prevention training and a free e-book, *Suicide: The Forever Decision*.

The Hope Line 1-800-394-4673 (HOPE). Hope Coaches are available 24/7, www.thehopeline.com.

Hope for the Heart 1-800-4673 (HOPE). Hope Care Representatives offer real answers for real people, www.hopefortheheart.org.

Survivors of Suicide, www.survivorsofsuicide.com. Offers links to help find support groups.

To Write Love on Her Arms, www.twloha.com, A non-profit movement dedicated to presenting hope and finding help for people struggling with depression, addiction, self-injury, and suicide.

Made in the USA
Monee, IL
17 October 2022

16056892R00083